Succeed in
Maths

Published by

Arcturus Publishing Limited

For Index Books Limited

Henson Way

Kettering

Northamptonshire

NN16 8PX

This edition published 2003

ISBN 1-84193-130-6

Printed and bound in China

Authors: Janet Smith, Janine Frost

Illustrator: Jim Hansen

Editor: Rebecca Panayiotou

Cover designer: Alex Ingr

Succeed in Maths

A simple and clear guide to understanding the principles of Mathematics.

Key Stage 2 Lower

Ages 7 to 9 years

Janet Smith

Janine Frost

INDEX

Introduction

Succeed in Maths is an invaluable guide and exercise book for both parents and teachers wishing to steer children through the enjoyable, although sometimes problematic, area of mathematics.

By the end of Key Stage 2, children should be able to handle numbers with ease; tackle fractions and decimals; understand the essentials of geometry; organise data, and understand measures.

This book looks carefully at these and other main topics of the National Curriculum with the objective of improving your child's understanding, speed and accuracy in mathematics.

The book is laid out so that a parent or teacher can help a child read through and understand the principles and methods of a topic on one page, while on the opposite page are exercises to test the child's understanding of these. The book has been designed so that most of the answers and workings out can be written straight on to the page. However, there are occasions when your child will need a working notebook.

Your child can work through this book at his/her own speed. A topic a day can be covered, or more if the child has the energy.

Each time your child has completed a page of this book, give them lots of praise and encouragement. Increase their sense of achievement by awarding them a star.

Within a short period of time you should find that your child approaches mathematics with improved confidence and understanding.

Good luck and good practising!

Contents

Place value

Value of digits

We can tell the ***value*** of a number by looking at the position of its ***digits***.

Look at the position of **2** in the examples below to see its place value.

Th	H	T	U	
			2	the **2** in the units column has a value of **two units = 2**
		2	0	the **2** in the tens column has the value of **two tens = 20**
	2	0	0	the **2** in the hundreds column has the value of **two hundreds = 200**
2	0	0	0	the **2** in the thousands column has the value of **two thousands = 2000**

So, in 3**4**2, the **4** has a value of **40** or **four tens**, in 4**6**02, the **6** has a value of **600** or **six hundreds**, and in 315**7**, the **7** has a value of **7** or **seven units**.

The zero acts as a ***placeholder***, to show that there is no value in a particular column.

E.g. in 402, the zero tells you there are no tens in this number.

Highest/lowest numbers

Now you have learnt about the position of the digits in a number, you can think about making numbers.

If we have the digits 2 and 6, we can make two numbers:

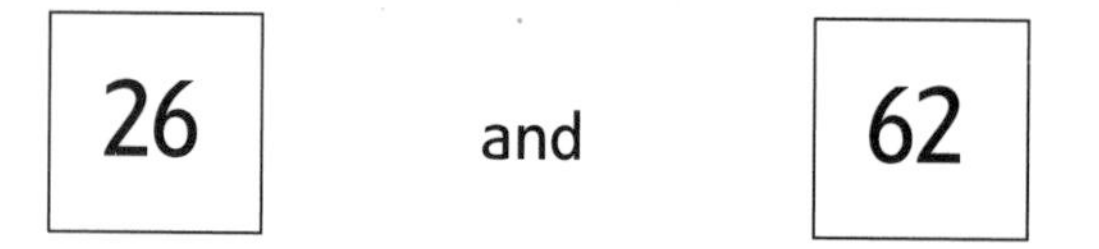

62 is the ***highest number*** we can make, and 26 is the ***lowest number*** we can make.

If we have the digits 3, 4, and 6, we can make:

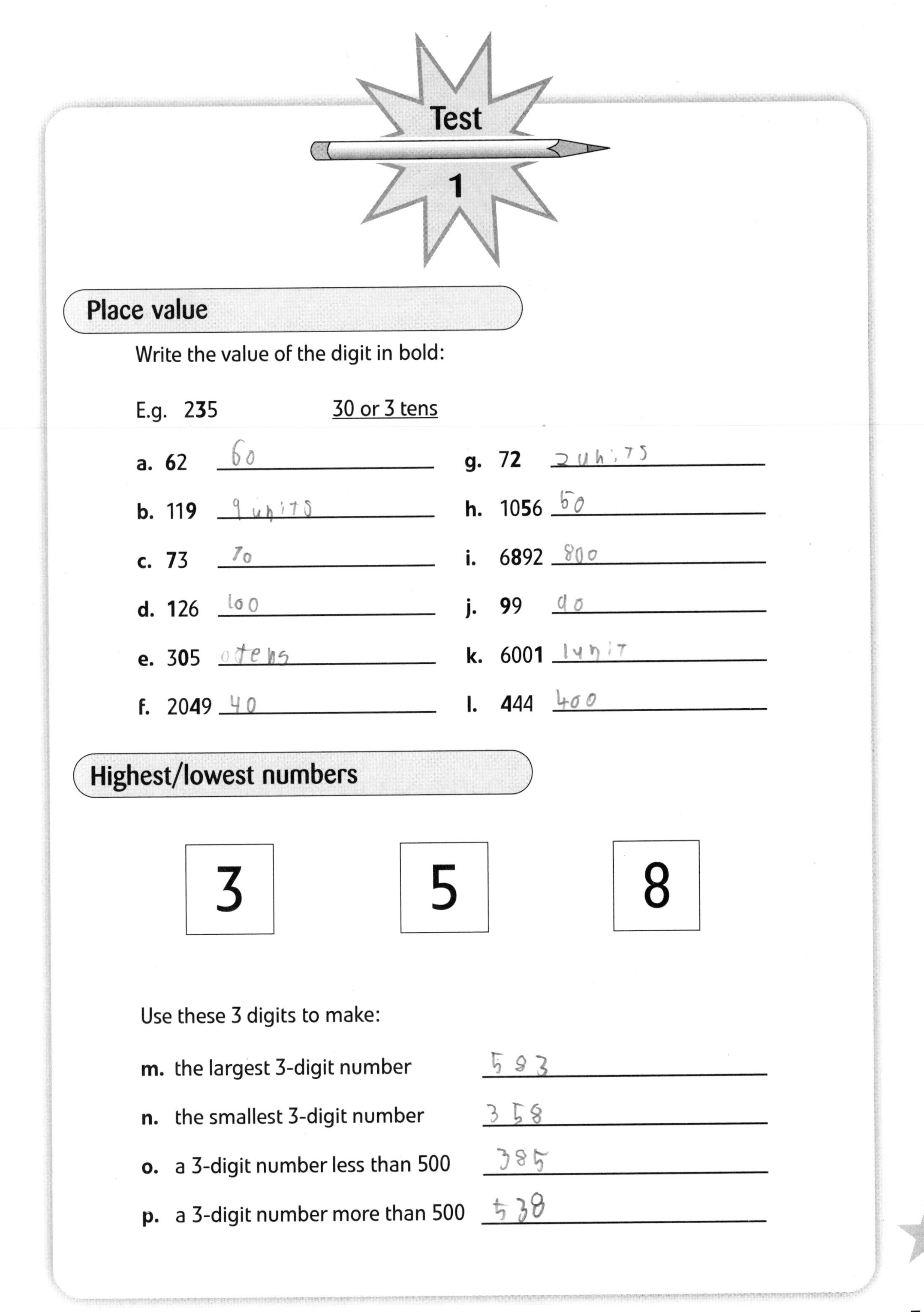

Test 1

Place value

Write the value of the digit in bold:

E.g. 235 <u>30 or 3 tens</u>

a. 62 60 ____________

b. 119 9 units ____________

c. 73 70 ____________

d. 126 100 ____________

e. 305 0 tens ____________

f. 2049 40 ____________

g. 72 2 units ____________

h. 1056 50 ____________

i. 6892 800 ____________

j. 99 90 ____________

k. 6001 1 unit ____________

l. 444 400 ____________

Highest/lowest numbers

3	5	8

Use these 3 digits to make:

m. the largest 3-digit number 583 ____________

n. the smallest 3-digit number 358 ____________

o. a 3-digit number less than 500 385 ____________

p. a 3-digit number more than 500 538 ____________

Partitioning

Partitioning

On page 6 we saw how a number has a value, based on the position of its digits.

Partitioning is when we take a number and ***split it*** to show the separate value of its digits.

E.g.

If we partition 43 we get:

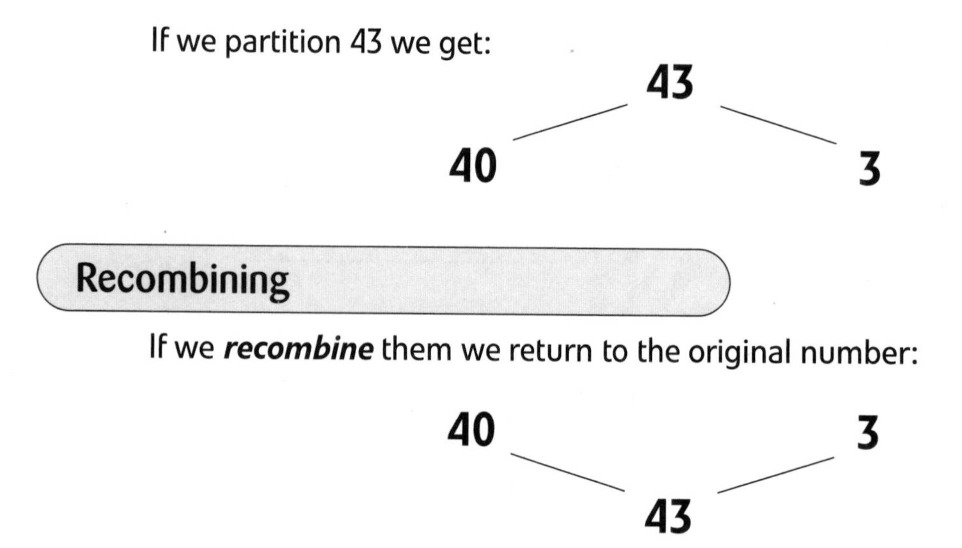

Recombining

If we ***recombine*** them we return to the original number:

40 3

43

Think of the zero in the 40 as 'hiding' behind the 3. The digit 4 is not worth four units – it is worth four tens or 40.

We can partition large numbers too:

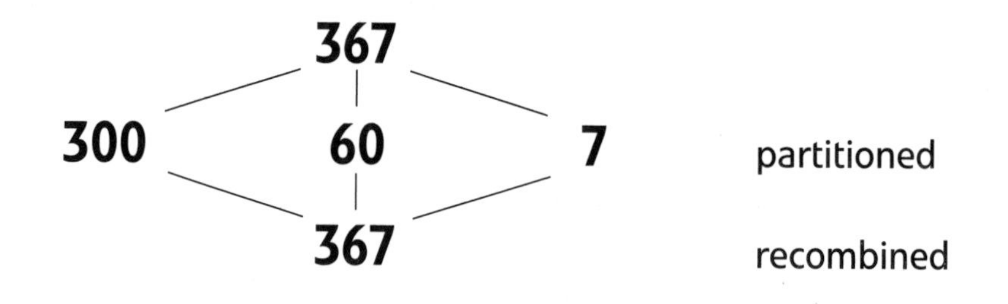

partitioned

recombined

This is a very important skill to understand and practise as it helps us to add, subtract, multiply and divide numbers in our heads, and using written methods.

Test 2

Partitioning

Partition these numbers:

a. 62 60 and 2 **d.** 58 50 and 8

b. 12 10 and 2 **e.** 79 7 and 9

c. 30 30 and 0 **f.** 84 80 and 4

Now try these:

g. 429 400 and 20 and 9

h. 632 600 and 30 and 2

i. 305 300 and 0 and 5

j. 222 200 and 20 and 2

Recombining

What numbers will you make if you recombine:

k. 90 and 6 96 **n.** 300 and 30 and 2 332

l. 40 and 2 42 **o.** 900 and 50 and 8 958

m. 60 and 8 68 **p.** 400 and 60 and 1 461

Rounding, greater than and less than

Rounding

When you ***round*** a number you express it ***approximately***, rather than precisely.

Method: To round a number to the nearest 10, you need to look at the unit digit and think about its position on a number line – which two multiples of 10 does it lie between?

E.g. 86 rounded to the nearest 10 is 90.
86 lies between 80 and 90, but is **nearer** to 90.

80	81	82	83	84	85	**86**	87	88	89	**90**
						nearer to 90				

E.g. 44 rounded to the nearest 10 is 40.
44 lies between 40 and 50, but is **nearer** to 40.

40	41	42	43	**44**	45	46	47	48	49	**50**
				nearer to 40						

If you have a number that ***ends in 5,*** i.e. it lies exactly halfway between the two multiples of 10, the rule is that you always ***round up*** to the next multiple of 10.

E.g. 65 rounded to the nearest 10 is 70.

Greater than/less than

As well as calculating with numbers, we can also compare them. We can look and see if they are ***greater than*** (larger) or ***less than*** each other.

E.g. 72 is greater than 12
567 is less than 1234
34 is less than 98

There are special mathematical symbols that we can use instead of always writing 'greater than' or 'less than'.

These are: $<$ and $>$

Try to remember that the larger number goes on the 'open' side of the symbol.

So: $72 > 12$ (72 is greater than 12) or $12 < 72$ (12 is less than 72)

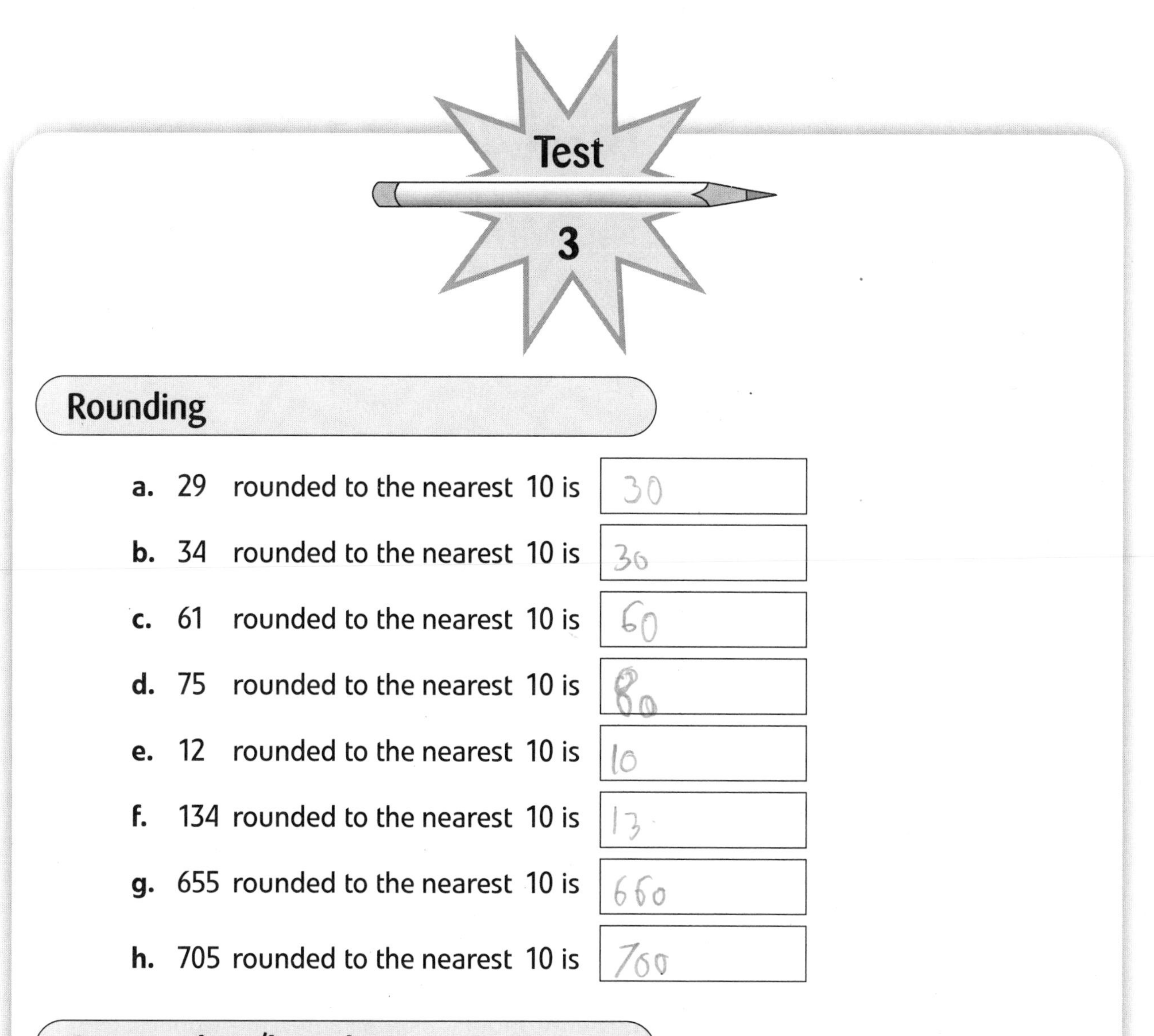

Test 3

Rounding

a. 29 rounded to the nearest 10 is [30]

b. 34 rounded to the nearest 10 is [30]

c. 61 rounded to the nearest 10 is [60]

d. 75 rounded to the nearest 10 is [80]

e. 12 rounded to the nearest 10 is [10]

f. 134 rounded to the nearest 10 is [13]

g. 655 rounded to the nearest 10 is [660]

h. 705 rounded to the nearest 10 is [700]

Greater than/less than

Write the symbol $>$ or $<$ in the boxes so that each number sentence reads correctly:

i. 36 [$>$] 22

j. 48 [$>$] 45

k. 13 [$<$] 500

l. 16 [$>$] 9

m. 178 [$<$] 179

n. 3456 [$<$] 5678

Are these statements true or false? Circle your answer.

o. $31 > 26$ T / F

p. $100 > 220$ T / F

q. $322 < 500$ T / F

r. $14 > 22$ T / F

s. $345 < 346$ T / F

t. $400 < 567$ T / F

Number pairs that total 10 and 20

In mathematics there are key facts that we need to learn by heart to help us calculate in our heads more quickly. These include times tables (up to the 10 times table), doubles and near doubles, and ***pairs that total 10 and 20***.

Pairs that total 10

$0 + 10 = 10$ $\quad$ $1 + 9 = 10$ $\quad$ $2 + 8 = 10$
$10 + 0 = 10$ $\quad$ $9 + 1 = 10$ $\quad$ $8 + 2 = 10$

$3 + 7 = 10$ $\quad$ $4 + 6 = 10$ $\quad$ $5 + 5 = 10$
$7 + 3 = 10$ $\quad$ $6 + 4 = 10$

You should look for these pairs when you are adding numbers together – seeing numbers that add quickly to 10 means you don't need to count on your fingers or use cubes – you know they make 10!

So if you saw 23 + 7, you could add the 3 and 7 quickly (which makes 10) and then add the 20 – so the total is 30.

Larger numbers

Knowing these pairs helps us with larger numbers, as the same 'rule' applies.

So if: $6 + 4 = 10$
it follows that: $60 + 40 = 100$ (each number is just 10 times bigger)

Similarly, if: $5 + 5 = 10$
it follows that: $50 + 50 = 100$

Pairs that total 20

$0 + 20 = 20$ $\quad$ $1 + 19 = 20$ $\quad$ $2 + 18 = 20$ $\quad$ $3 + 17 = 20$
$20 + 0 = 20$ $\quad$ $19 + 1 = 20$ $\quad$ $18 + 2 = 20$ $\quad$ $17 + 3 = 20$

$4 + 16 = 20$ $\quad$ $5 + 15 = 20$ $\quad$ $6 + 14 = 20$ $\quad$ $7 + 13 = 20$
$16 + 4 = 20$ $\quad$ $15 + 5 = 20$ $\quad$ $14 + 6 = 20$ $\quad$ $13 + 7 = 20$

$8 + 12 = 20$ $\quad$ $9 + 11 = 20$ $\quad$ $10 + 10 = 20$
$12 + 8 = 20$ $\quad$ $11 + 9 = 20$

Do you notice any similarities here with the pairs of numbers that total 10?

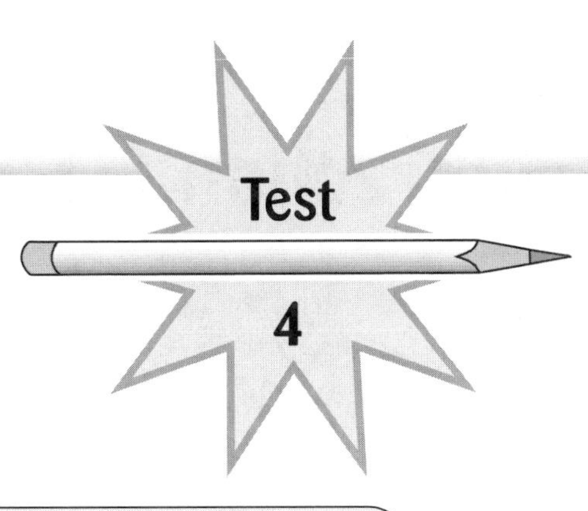

Pairs that total 10

When you are ready, cover up the page opposite and try these:

a. 3 + 7 = 10 **e.** 10 + 0 = 10

b. 8 + 2 = 10 **f.** 5 + 5 = 10

c. 4 + 6 = 10 **g.** 0 + 10 = 10

d. 1 + 9 = 10 **h.** 2 + 8 = 10

Can you complete these subtraction questions, using your knowledge of the pairs?

i. 10 – 7 = 3 **l.** 10 – 4 = 6

j. 10 – 5 = 5 **m.** 10 – 2 = 8

k. 10 – 9 = 1 **n.** 10 – 8 = 2

Can you work these out in your head? Look for pairs that total 10 to help!

o. 23 + 7 = 30 **r.** 34 + 6 = 40

p. 45 + 5 = 50 **s.** 67 + 3 = 60

q. 21 + 9 = 30 **t.** 84 + 6 = 80

Pairs that total 20

u. 17 + 3 = 20 **x.** 12 + 8 = 20

v. 14 + 6 = 20 **y.** 6 + 14 = 20

w. 2 + 18 = 20 **z.** 19 + 1 = 20

Addition and subtraction (1)

Addition using partitioning

You will remember from page 8 that numbers can be partitioned.

We can use this to help us add and subtract larger numbers, either in our head or using pencil and paper.

Method: Consider the question $24 + 32 = ?$

By partitioning the numbers we can add the tens together, then the units and then recombine the two for the final answer.

So:	24		+	32	
Partition:	20 +	4	+	30 +	2
Add the tens:	20 +	30	=	50	
Add the units:	4 +	2	=	6	
Total (recombine):	50 +	6	=	56	

Larger numbers

This method also works for larger numbers:

Consider:		324		+		568		
Partition:	300 +	20 +	4	+	500 +	60 +	8	
Add the hundreds:	300 +	500	=	800				
Add the tens:	20 +	60	=	80				
Add the units:	4 +	8	=	12				
Total (recombine):	800 +	80	+	12	=	892		

As you practise this calculation strategy you may find that you don't need to write down all the different stages all of the time – some of it you might be able to work out in your head.

Test 5

Addition using partitioning

Practise the method:

a. 62 + 35

Partition:	60	+	2	+	30	+	5
Add the tens:	60	+	30	=	90		
Add the units:	6	+	5	=	19		
Recombine the tens and units:	62	+	35	=	109		

Now try these. You may need to use a separate piece of paper for your workings.

b. 58 + 21 = 79

c. 76 + 17 = 93

d. 24 + 68 = 92

e. 43 + 35 = 78

f. 61 + 27 = 88

g. 35 + 41 = 76

Larger numbers

Using the same method as above, try these:

h. 125 + 241 = 366

i. 232 + 423 = 655

j. 611 + 275 = 886

k. 503 + 269 = 772

Addition and subtraction (2)

Subtraction using partitioning

You have practised using partitioning to help you add two numbers together. We will now look at how it could help you to subtract numbers.

Method: Consider the question 56 - 33 = ?

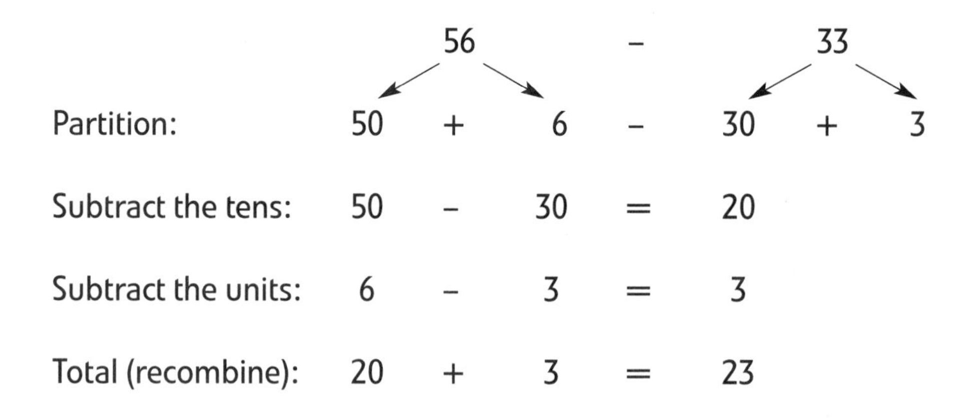

Subtraction using a number line

However, this method is not always the best for subtraction. Let us look at another strategy, using a ***number line***.

Method: Consider 35 – 13 = ?

Think of the position of these numbers on a number line. The answer to the question can be calculated by working out the distance between the two numbers, or by finding ***the difference*** between them.

Mark the two numbers on a blank number line. Mark on any multiples of 10 (on other occasions it might be multiples of 100).

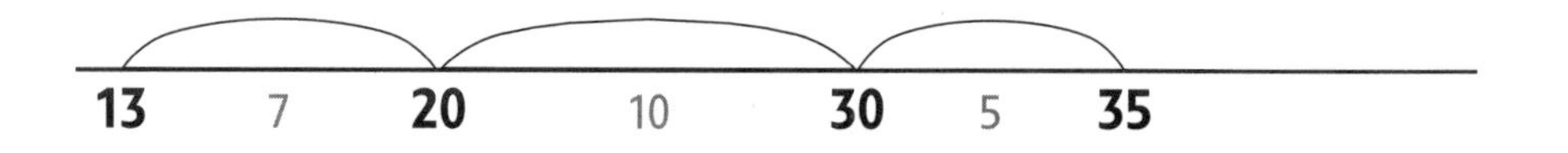

By marking in the multiples of 10, we can then work out the value of the 'jumps' between the numbers. Then we add these together to work out the full distance between them.

7 + 10 + 5 = 22

So: 35 - 13 = 22

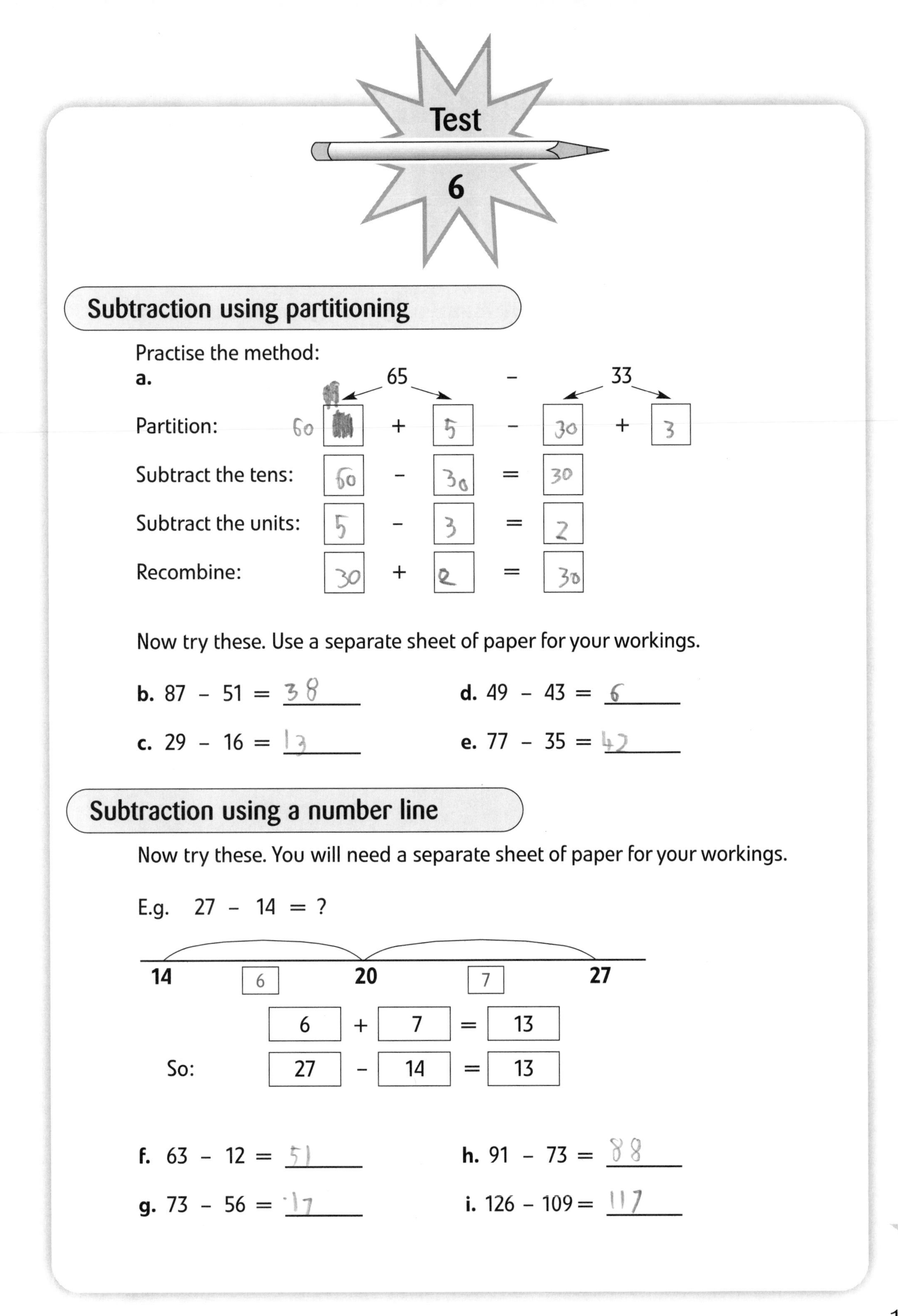

Test 6

Subtraction using partitioning

Practise the method:

a. 65 – 33

Partition:	60	+	5	–	30	+	3
Subtract the tens:	60	–	30	=	30		
Subtract the units:	5	–	3	=	2		
Recombine:	30	+	2	=	30		

Now try these. Use a separate sheet of paper for your workings.

b. 87 – 51 = 38

c. 29 – 16 = 13

d. 49 – 43 = 6

e. 77 – 35 = 42

Subtraction using a number line

Now try these. You will need a separate sheet of paper for your workings.

E.g. 27 – 14 = ?

14 [6] **20** [7] **27**

6 + 7 = 13

So: 27 – 14 = 13

f. 63 – 12 = 51

g. 73 – 56 = 17

h. 91 – 73 = 88

i. 126 – 109 = 117

Addition and subtraction (3)

Addition using a number line

We have looked at how a number line can help us to work out the difference between two numbers.

We can also use it to practise another strategy for adding two numbers.

Counting on in tens and units

Method: Consider $34 + 25 = ?$

If we partition the second number we can see that we are being asked to add two tens, or 20, and five units, or 5.

On a blank number line write the starting number (34):

34

Then count on the two tens:

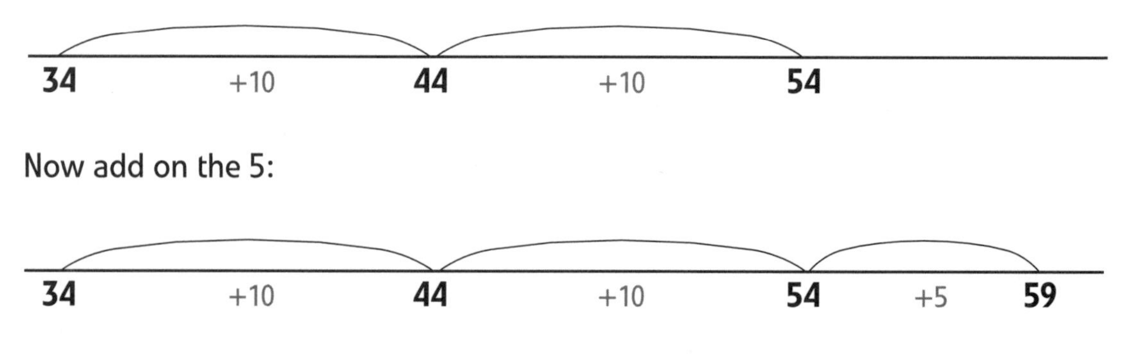

Now add on the 5:

So the answer to $34 + 25$ is 59.

The idea is that you can use the number line to practise this strategy, but that eventually you can work sums out in your head, counting on in tens first and then adding the units.

Test

7

Addition using a number line

a. 23 + 32 = 55

b. 56 + 23 = 79

c. 45 + 14 = 59

d. 86 + 13 = 99

e. 129 + 21 = 130

f. 234 + 35 = 269

Doubling and halving

Doubling

Doubling means to ***multiply a number by 2*** – so double 4 is 8 (4 x 2), double 16 is 32 (16 x 2) and double 100 is 200 (100 x 2).

However, you can also calculate the double of a number ***by adding it to itself*** – so double 9 is 18 (9 + 9), double 10 is 20 (10 + 10) and double 300 is 600 (300 + 300).

Doubling twice

If you double a number, then double again, you are actually ***multiplying the number by 4***. This is a good rule to learn if you have problems remembering your 4 times table.

E.g. If you wanted to calculate 4 x 6, you can double the 6, then double again:

$$6 \times 2 = 12$$
$$12 \times 2 = 24$$

So: $4 \times 6 = 24$

Halving

Halving is the opposite of doubling, and means ***divide a number by 2***.

So half of 8 is 4 (8 ÷ 2), half of 32 is 16 (32 ÷ 2) and half of 200 is 100 (200 ÷ 2).

Halving twice

If you halve a number, then halve again, you are ***dividing it by 4***.

E.g. If you wanted to calculate 100 ÷ 4, you can halve the 100, then halve again:

$$100 \div 2 = 50$$
$$50 \div 2 = 25$$

So: $100 \div 4 = 25$

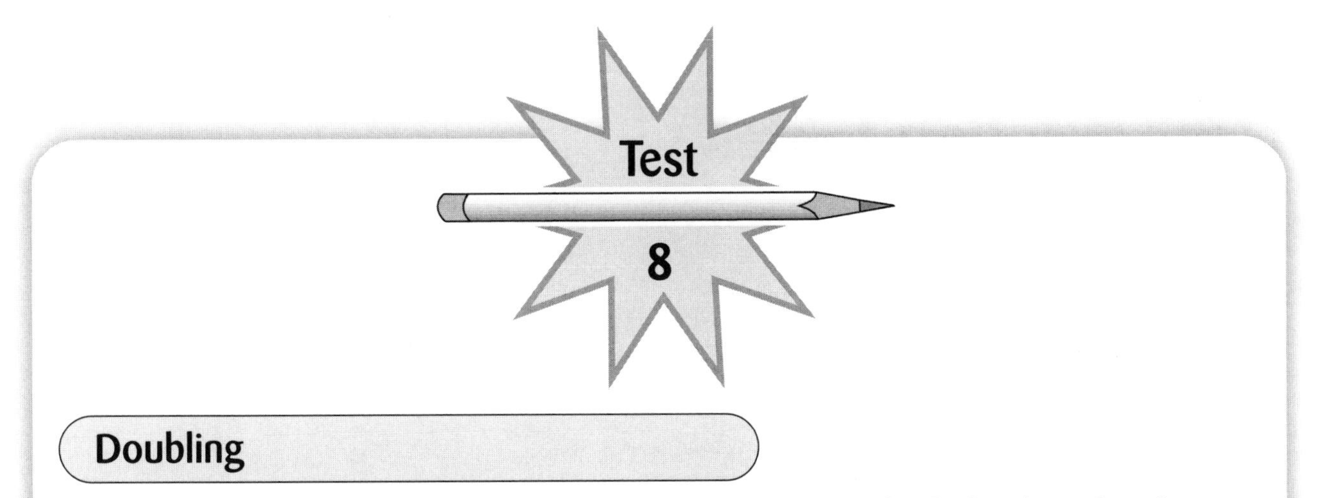

Doubling

Double the numbers in Set A and find the answer in Set B. One has already been done for you.

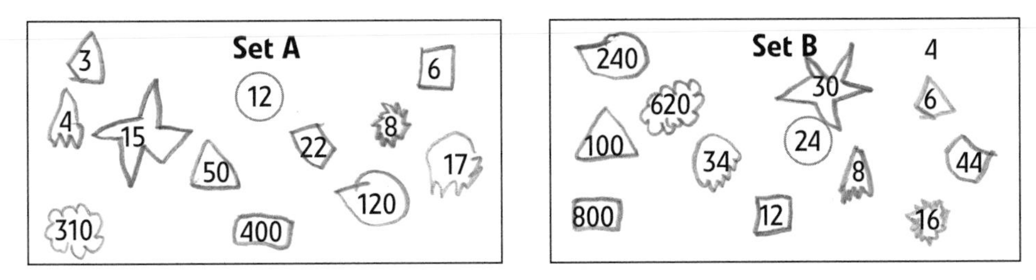

Using the double and double again method, try these:

a. 8 x 4 = 32   **e.** 12 x 4 = 48

b. 30 x 4 = 120   **f.** 25 x 4 = 100

c. 14 x 4 = 56   **g.** 110 x 4 = 440

d. 41 x 4 = 164   **h.** 150 x 4 = 600

Halving

i. 10 ÷ 2 = 5   **l.** 50 ÷ 2 = 25

j. 16 ÷ 2 = 8   **m.** 100 ÷ 2 = 50

k. 20 ÷ 2 = 10   **n.** 200 ÷ 2 = 100

Using the halve and halve again method, try these:

o. 20 ÷ 4 = 5   **r.** 60 ÷ 4 = 15

p. 40 ÷ 4 = 10   **s.** 100 ÷ 4 = 25

q. 48 ÷ 4 = 12   **t.** 420 ÷ 4 = 105

Multiplication tables

Multiplication

Multiplication makes a set bigger. So, for example, a set of 8 can be doubled by multiplying by 2:

8 multiplied by 2 = 16
8 lots of 2 = 16
8 times 2 = 16
8 x 2 = 16

Similarly, a set of 4 can be made 10 times larger by multiplying by 10:

4 multiplied by 10 = 40
4 lots of 10 = 40
4 times 10 = 40
4 x 10 = 40

Repeated addition

10 lots of 4 is the same as **4 + 4 + 4 + 4 + 4 + 4 + 4 + 4 + 4 + 4.**
4 is added to 4 ten times.

This is another way that we can calculate our times tables. We need to learn to count in 2s, 3s, 4s, 5s and 10s – this will help us to calculate multiplication tables quickly.

1 x 2 = 2	1 x 3 = 3	1 x 4 = 4	1 x 5 = 5
2 x 2 = 4	2 x 3 = 6	2 x 4 = 8	2 x 5 = 10
3 x 2 = 6	3 x 3 = 9	3 x 4 = 12	3 x 5 = 15
4 x 2 = 8	4 x 3 = 12	4 x 4 = 16	4 x 5 = 20
5 x 2 = 10	5 x 3 = 15	5 x 4 = 20	5 x 5 = 25
6 x 2 = 12	6 x 3 = 18	6 x 4 = 24	6 x 5 = 30
7 x 2 = 14	7 x 3 = 21	7 x 4 = 28	7 x 5 = 35
8 x 2 = 16	8 x 3 = 24	8 x 4 = 32	8 x 5 = 40
9 x 2 = 18	9 x 3 = 27	9 x 4 = 36	9 x 5 = 45
10 x 2 = 20	10 x 3 = 30	10 x 4 = 40	10 x 5 = 50

Multiplication

Test your tables knowledge – cover up the page opposite and see if you can remember your 3 times table, 4 times table and 5 times table.

1 x 3 = 3	1 x 4 =	1 x 5 = 5
2 x = 6	2 x 8	2 x 5 = 10
3 x = 9	3 x 12	3 x 5 = 15
4 x = 12	4 x 16	4 x 5 = 20
5 x = 15	5 x 20	5 x 5 = 25
6 x = 18	6 x 24	6 x 5 = 30
7 x = 21	7 x 28	7 x 5 = 35
8 x = 24	8 x 32	8 x 5 = 40
9 x = 27	9 x 36	9 x 5 = 45
10 x = 30	10 x 4	10 x 5 = 5

Repeated addition

Finish these number patterns:

a. 2, 4, 6, 8, 10, 12, 14, 16, 18, 20

b. 5, 10, 15, 20, 25, 30, 35, 40, 45, 50

c. 3, 6, 9, 12, 15, 18, 21, 24, 27, 30

d. 4, 8, 12, 16, 20, 24, 28, 32, 36, 40

Inverse operations

Inverse operations

An ***inverse operation*** is an ***opposite calculation***. Addition and subtraction are inverse operations. This can be illustrated on a number line, starting with 7:

7 + 4 = 11

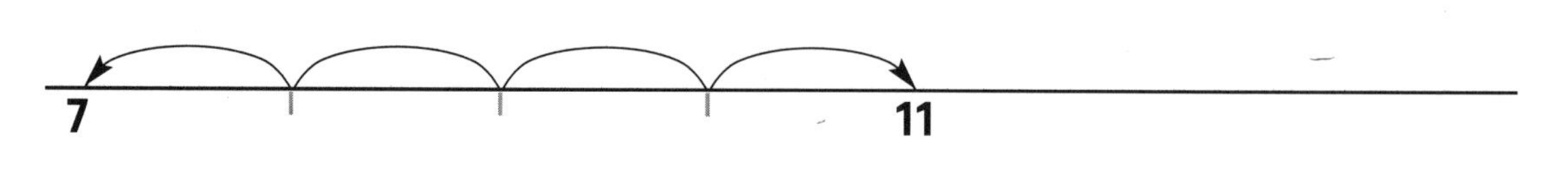

11 - 7 = 4

Similarly, multiplication and division are inverse operations.

2 lots of 7 = 14   2 x 7 = 14

14 shared between 2 sets = 7   14 ÷ 2 = 7

Number families

Number families are three numbers that make inverse number sentences.

E.g. 4, 7, 11
4 + 7 = 11
7 + 4 = 11
11 - 7 = 4
11 - 4 = 7

2, 7, 14
2 x 7 = 14
7 x 2 = 14
14 ÷ 2 = 7
14 ÷ 7 = 2

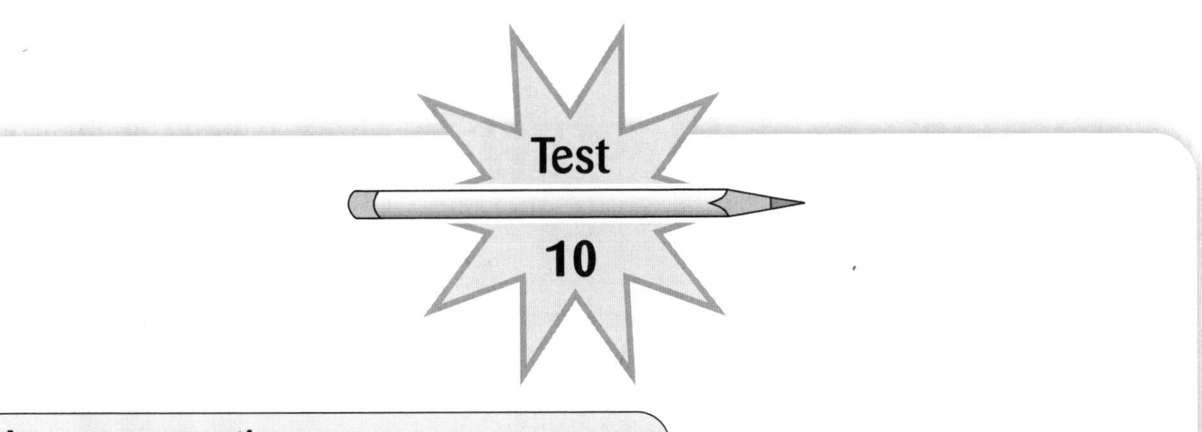

Inverse operations

Complete the inverse operations of these number sentences in order to work out the missing number:

E.g. 1 + [9] = 10   10 – 1 = 9   Therefore the missing number is [9].

a. 12 + [ ] = 24 ________

b. [ ] + 14 = 39 ________

c. 17 + [ ] = 43 ________

d. 26 = [ ] + 9 ________

e. 58 = 27 + [ ] ________

f. 63 + [ ] = 98 ________

g. 27 + [ ] = 57 ________

h. 7 x [ ] = 28 ________

i. [ ] x 3 = 15 ________

j. 5 x [ ] = 35 ________

k. [ ] x 2 = 24 ________

l. 10 x [ ] = 40 ________

m. 32 = [ ] x 4 ________

n. 55 = 11 x [ ] ________

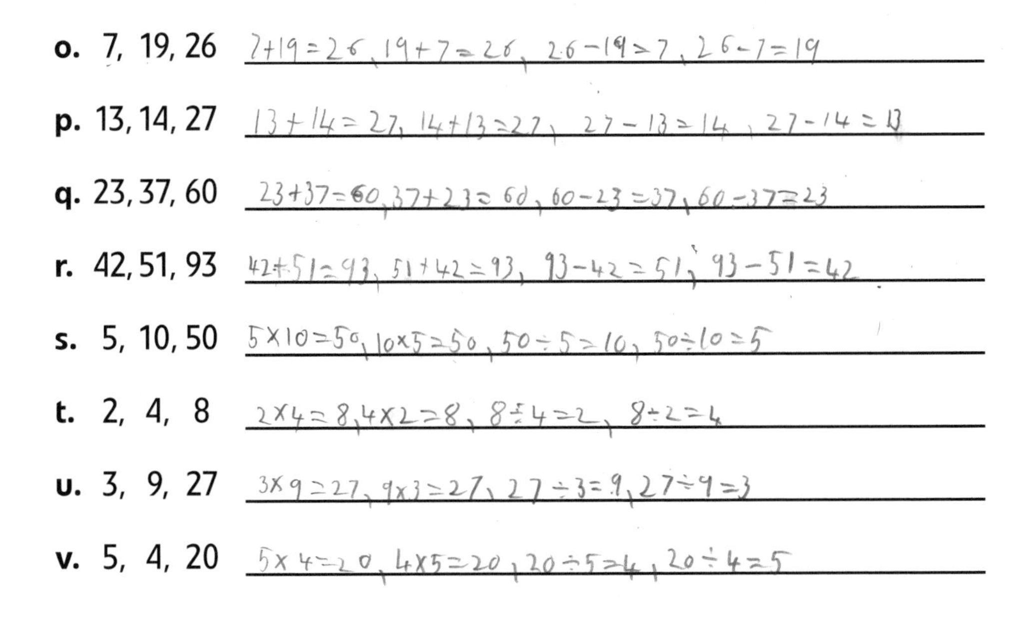

Use each of these number families to make four number sentences:

o. 7, 19, 26 ________

p. 13, 14, 27 ________

q. 23, 37, 60 ________

r. 42, 51, 93 ________

s. 5, 10, 50 ________

t. 2, 4, 8 ________

u. 3, 9, 27 ________

v. 5, 4, 20 ________

Multiplication with larger numbers

Using partitioning

We have shown how partitioning numbers can help us with our addition and subtraction strategies. In multiplication it can help us to break our calculations down into stages.

Method: Consider 16 x 5 = ?

We know we can partition the 16 into 10 and 6. Each part can now be multiplied by the 5, and then the two results can be added back together to get the answer.

So: 10 x 5 = 50
6 x 5 = 30
50 + 30 = 80

So: 16 x 5 = 80

Grid method

We can record this method (using partitioning) in a different way to help us 'keep track' of the stages involved, and make sure we don't miss part of the calculation.

This recording uses a ***grid*** to show each part.

Consider 25 x 3 = ?

If we partition the 25 we get 20 and 5. Each part is now multiplied by the 3.

Layout:

x	20	5
3	60	15

(25 partitioned)

(20 x 3) (5 x 3)

The answer is the two numbers in the boxes added together: 60 + 15 = 75.

We can also use the grid method for larger numbers.

E.g. 325 x 2

x	300	20	5
2	600	40	10

600 + 40 + 10 = 650

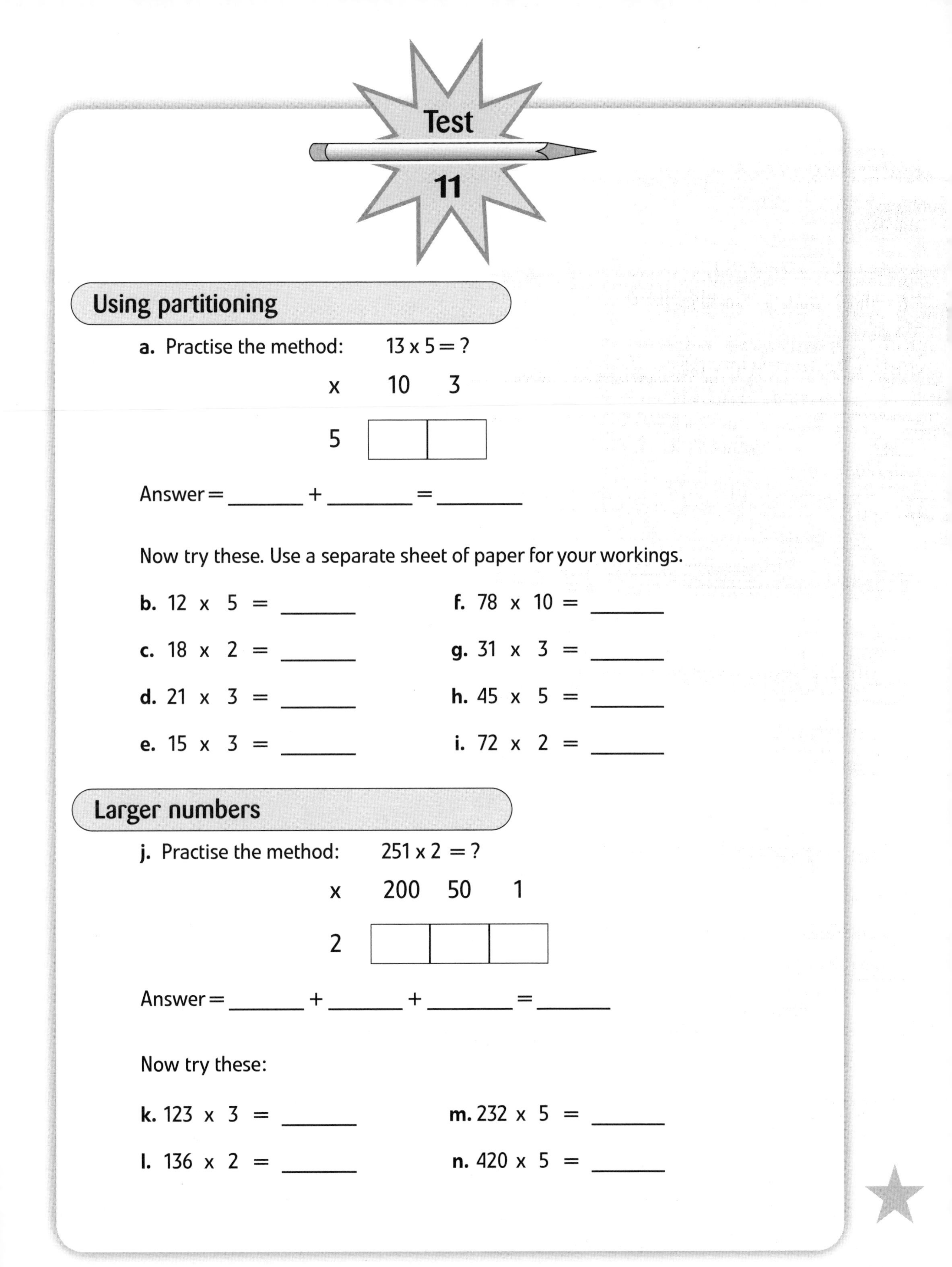

Test 11

Using partitioning

a. Practise the method: 13 x 5 = ?

x	10	3
5		

Answer = _______ + _______ = _______

Now try these. Use a separate sheet of paper for your workings.

b. 12 x 5 = _______

c. 18 x 2 = _______

d. 21 x 3 = _______

e. 15 x 3 = _______

f. 78 x 10 = _______

g. 31 x 3 = _______

h. 45 x 5 = _______

i. 72 x 2 = _______

Larger numbers

j. Practise the method: 251 x 2 = ?

x	200	50	1
2			

Answer = _______ + _______ + _______ = _______

Now try these:

k. 123 x 3 = _______

l. 136 x 2 = _______

m. 232 x 5 = _______

n. 420 x 5 = _______

Division

Division means to group or share a number by another given number. It is the inverse of multiplication.

Symbols and vocabulary

The mathematical symbol for division is ÷

8 ÷ 2 can be said as:

8 ***divided by*** 2
8 ***shared equally between*** 2
8 ***grouped into*** 2s

In all these examples the 2 is the ***divisor***, and the 8 is the ***dividend***.

Sharing and grouping will lead to the same result, but the mathematics involved is slightly different.

Sharing equally

If we shared 8 sweets between 2 people they would get 4 each:

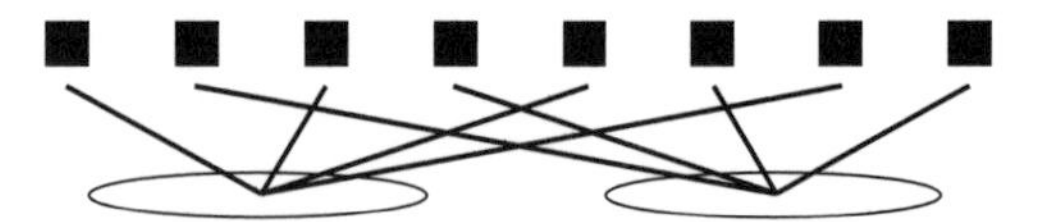

Here, each person is given one sweet each until there are no more to share out.

Grouping or repeated subtraction

Here, we take out groups of the divisor from the dividend.

So 8 ÷ 2 means – how many groups of 2 are there in 8?

Here, we have taken out groups of 2 until there is nothing left – and we make 4 groups.

Using sharing to calculate division problems becomes difficult with larger numbers – imagine having 2000 sweets to share between 5 people. If we gave each person one sweet each until they all ran out we would be there for a very long time! With larger numbers it is easier to use grouping.

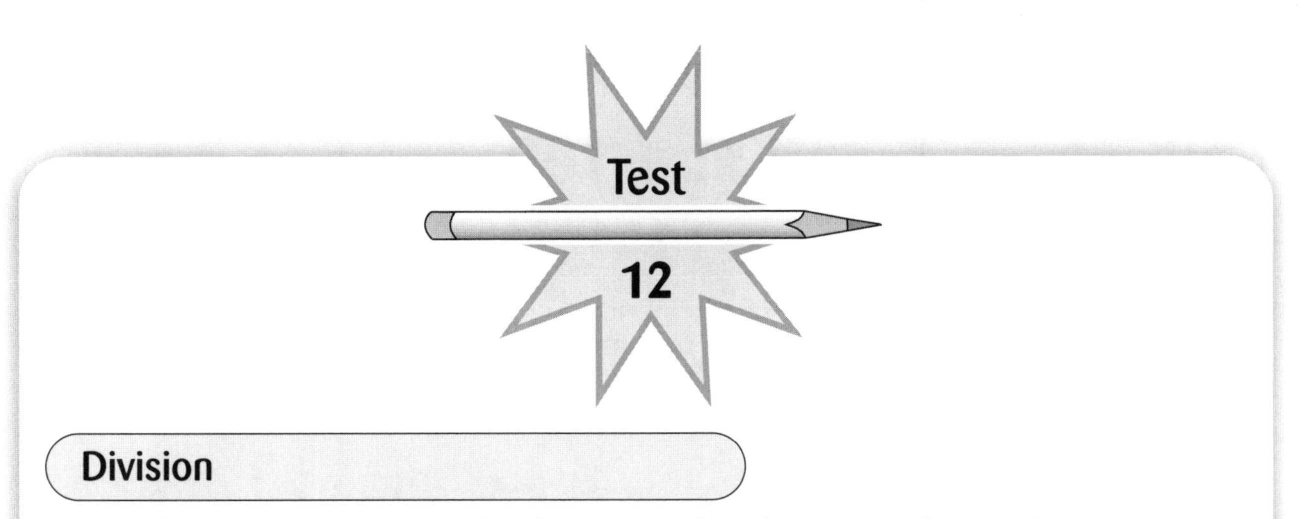

Division

Division is the inverse of multiplication. Use these multiplication facts to write the inverse division facts.

E.g. If 4 x 5 = 20 then 20 ÷ 4 = 5 or 20 ÷ 5 = 4

a. If 6 x 5 = 30 then ____________ or ____________

b. If 2 x 8 = 16 then ____________ or ____________

c. If 7 x 5 = 35 then ____________ or ____________

d. If 10 x 5 = 50 then ____________ or ____________

Now try these – you can use the multiplication table in the back of the book to help you, or draw some diagrams!

e. 27 ÷ 3 = ____________

f. 12 ÷ 2 = ____________

g. 15 ÷ 5 = ____________

h. 18 ÷ 3 = ____________

i. 50 ÷ 10 = ____________

Fill in the missing boxes:

j. □ ÷ 5 = 5

k. 18 ÷ □ = 9

l. 120 ÷ 10 = □

m. □ ÷ 2 = 8

Multiplying by 10 and 100

Multiplying by 10

When we multiply a number by 10 it becomes ***ten times bigger***.

So: 1 x 10 = 10
2 x 10 = 20
3 x 10 = 30 and so on.

We can use the place value chart from earlier on (see page 6) to see what happens to the digits in a number when it is multiplied by 10.

H	T	U	
		1	multiplied by 10 is
	1	0	multiplied by 10 is
1	0	0	

Notice how each time, the digit **'1'** moves ***one place to the left***.

We need to use the zero as a placeholder to show that there are no units, or no tens and units.

We can use this rule to help us multiply any number by 10.

E.g. 43 x 10 = 430

H	T	U	
	4	**3**	each digit moves one place to the left
4	**3**	0	← zero is needed to show there are no units

Multiplying by 100

When we multiply a number by 100 it becomes ***a hundred times bigger***.

If we multiply 6 by 100 we get 600.

H	T	U	
		6	multiplied by 100 is
6	0	0	

The digit **'6'** has moved ***two places to the left***.

This is the rule for multiplying by 100.

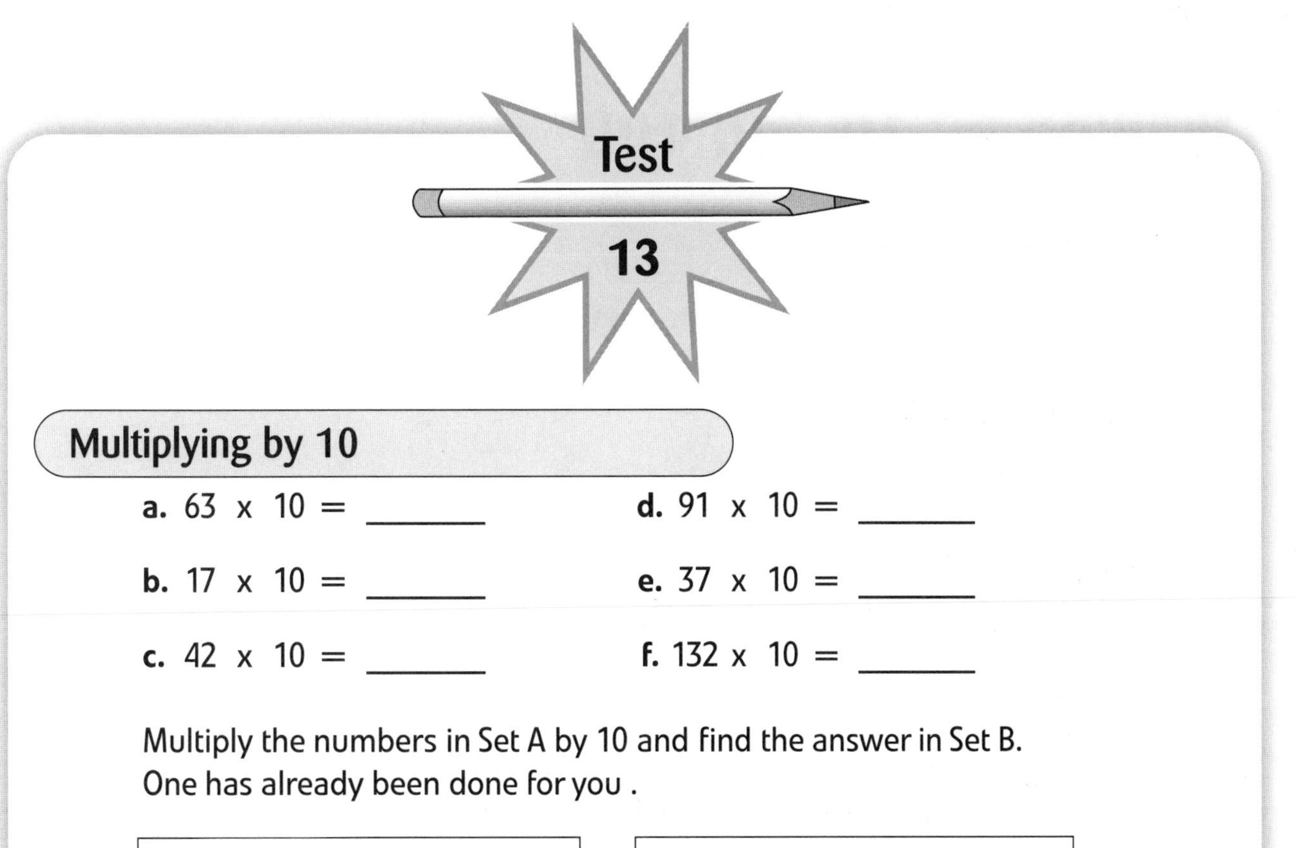

Multiplying by 10

a. 63 x 10 = ______ **d.** 91 x 10 = ______

b. 17 x 10 = ______ **e.** 37 x 10 = ______

c. 42 x 10 = ______ **f.** 132 x 10 = ______

Multiply the numbers in Set A by 10 and find the answer in Set B.
One has already been done for you .

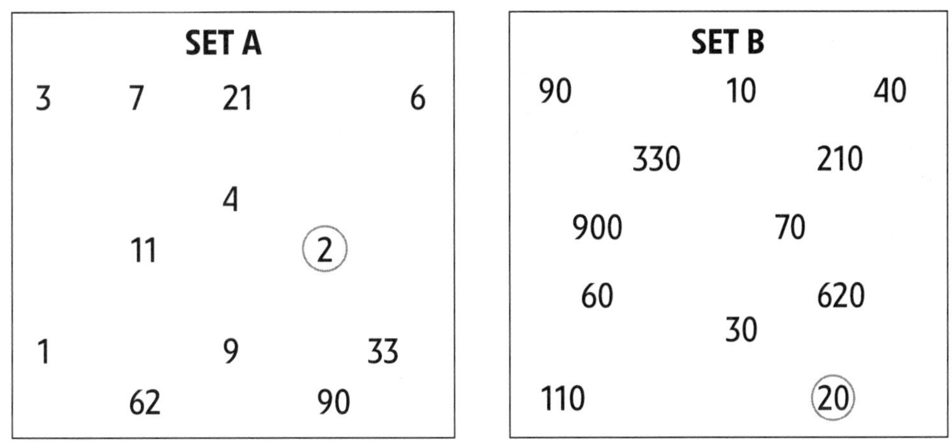

Multiplying by 100

g. 4 x 100 = ______ **j.** 22 x 100 = ______

h. 7 x 100 = ______ **k.** 38 x 100 = ______

i. 18 x 100 = ______ **l.** 72 x 100 = ______

Complete these two statements:

m. To multiply a number by 10, move all its digits ______ place to the ______.

n. To multiply a number by 100, move all its digits ______ places to the ______.

Dividing by 10 and 100

Dividing by 10

When we divide a number by 10 it becomes ***ten times smaller***.

So: $10 \div 10 = 1$
$20 \div 10 = 2$
$30 \div 10 = 3$ and so on.

When we look at what happens using the place value chart, we see that the digits in a number all move ***one place to the right***.

H	T	U	
1	0	0	divided by 10 is
	1	0	divided by 10 is
		1	

We can use this rule to help us divide any number by 10.

E.g. $640 \div 10 = 64$

H	T	U	
6	4	0	
	6	4	each digit moves one place to the right

Dividing by 100

When we divide a number by 100 it becomes ***a hundred times smaller***.

So, if we divide 3200 by 100 we get:

Th	H	T	U	
3	2	0	0	divided by 100 is
		3	2	

The digits have moved ***two places to the right***.

This is the rule for dividing by 100.

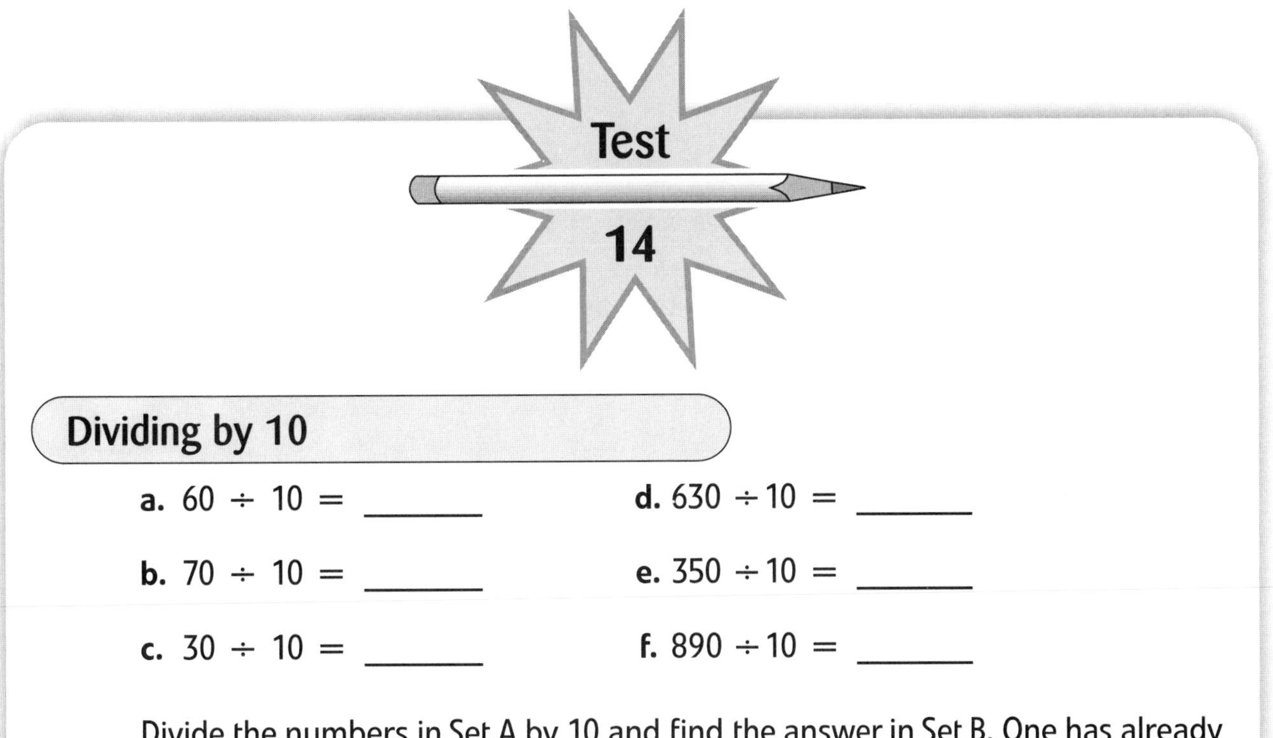

Dividing by 10

a. 60 ÷ 10 = ______

b. 70 ÷ 10 = ______

c. 30 ÷ 10 = ______

d. 630 ÷ 10 = ______

e. 350 ÷ 10 = ______

f. 890 ÷ 10 = ______

Divide the numbers in Set A by 10 and find the answer in Set B. One has already been done for you.

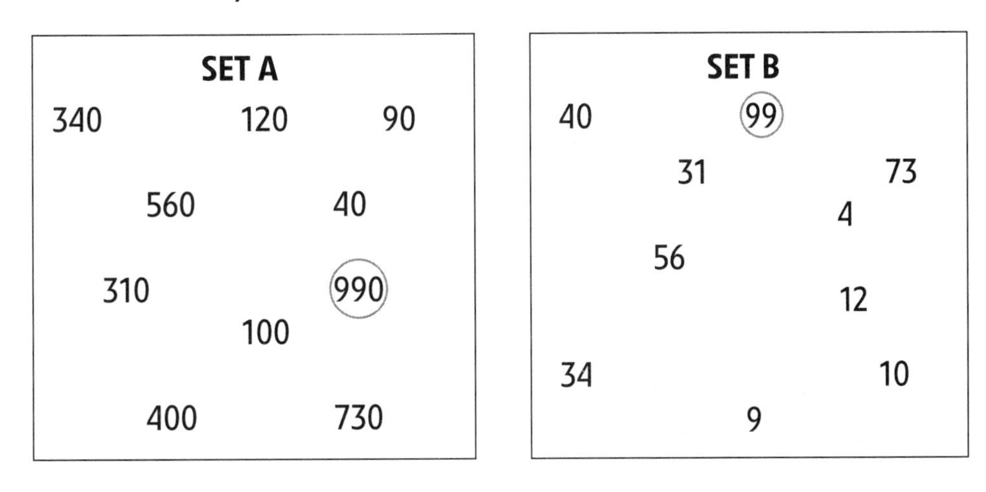

Dividing by 100

g. 400 ÷ 100 = ______

h. 900 ÷ 100 = ______

i. 300 ÷ 100 = ______

j. 3200 ÷ 100 = ______

k. 9900 ÷ 100 = ______

l. 4100 ÷ 100 = ______

Complete these two statements:

m. To divide a number by 10, move all its digits ______ place to the ______ .

n. To divide a number by 100, move all its digits ______ places to the ______ .

Fabulous facts

Odds and evens

Numbers that can be divided equally by 2 are called ***even numbers***.

So: 2, 4, 6, 8, 10, 12, 14, 16, 18... etc are even numbers. Zero is also an even number.

Numbers that cannot be divided by 2 are called ***odd numbers***.

So: 1, 3, 5, 7, 9, 11, 13, 15, 17... etc are odd numbers.

To spot an even or odd number, look at the units digit:

If it is a 0, 2, 4, 6, or 8, the number is even.
If it is a 1, 3, 5, 7, or 9, the number is odd.

Multiples and factors

A ***multiple*** is a number that can be divided by another given number.

E.g. 5, 10 and 15 can all be divided by 5, so are called ***multiples of 5***.
3, 6 and 9 can all be divided by 3, or are in the 3 times table,
so these are called ***multiples of 3***.

A ***factor*** is any number that can be divided exactly into a given number.

E.g. The factors of 12 are 1, 2, 3, 4, 6 and 12
The factors of 17 are 1 and 17
The factors of 32 are 1, 2, 4, 8, 16, and 32

Number sequences

Numbers can be written in a variety of ***sequences***, or ***patterns*** – we have to look for clues to see what the pattern is and predict the next numbers in the pattern.

E.g. 1, 4, 7, 10, 13...

Each number is 3 more than the last one, so the next number would be 13 + 3, which is 16.

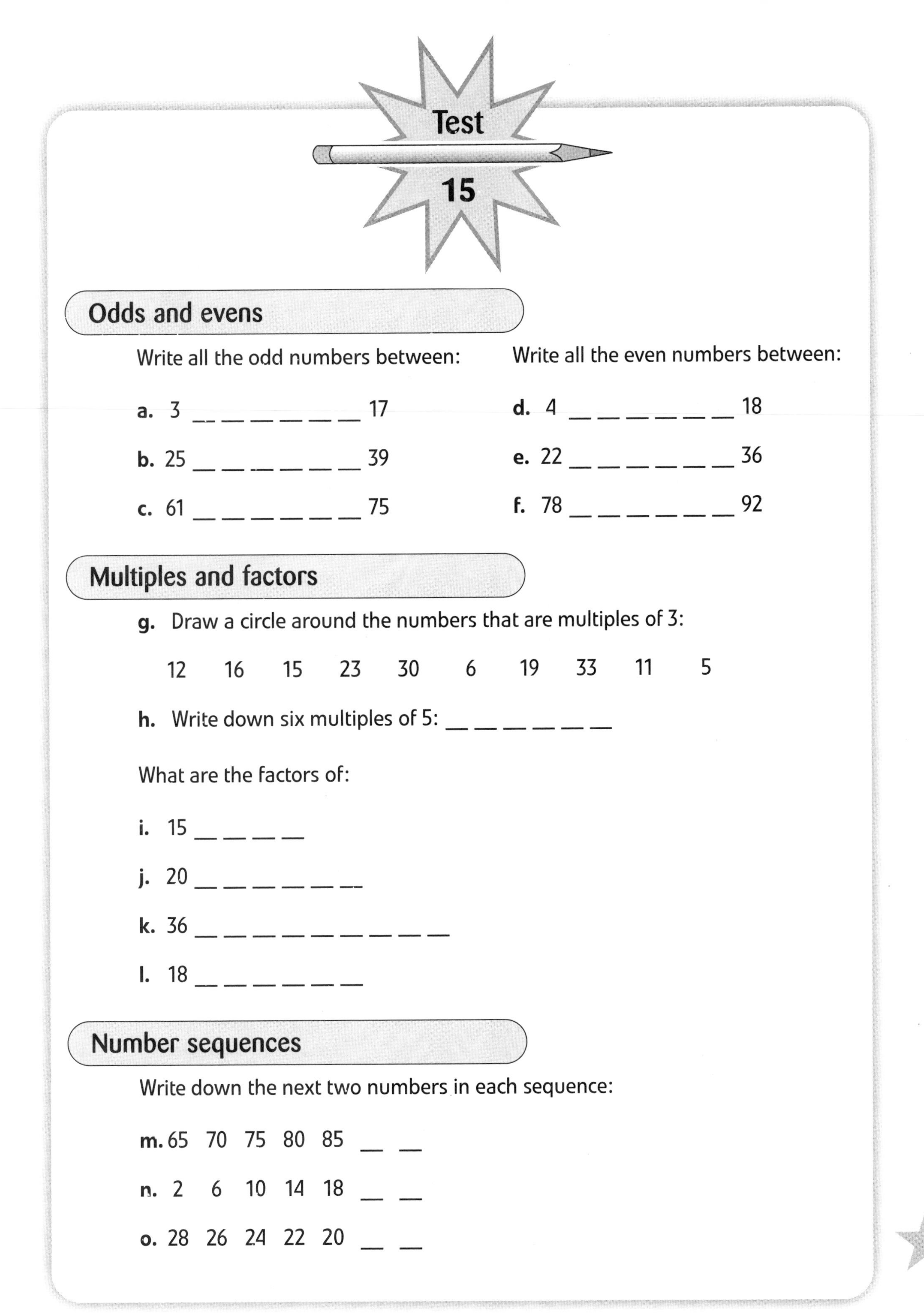

Test 15

Odds and evens

Write all the odd numbers between:

a. 3 __ __ __ __ __ __ 17

b. 25 __ __ __ __ __ __ 39

c. 61 __ __ __ __ __ __ 75

Write all the even numbers between:

d. 4 __ __ __ __ __ __ 18

e. 22 __ __ __ __ __ __ 36

f. 78 __ __ __ __ __ __ 92

Multiples and factors

g. Draw a circle around the numbers that are multiples of 3:

12 16 15 23 30 6 19 33 11 5

h. Write down six multiples of 5: __ __ __ __ __ __

What are the factors of:

i. 15 __ __ __ __

j. 20 __ __ __ __ __ __

k. 36 __ __ __ __ __ __ __ __ __

l. 18 __ __ __ __ __ __

Number sequences

Write down the next two numbers in each sequence:

m. 65 70 75 80 85 __ __

n. 2 6 10 14 18 __ __

o. 28 26 24 22 20 __ __

Recognising simple fractions

Fractions

A ***fraction*** is a part of something.
The most common fraction is a ***half***, which is 1 of 2 equal parts and can be written as $\frac{1}{2}$.

The top number of a fraction is the ***numerator***, and the lower number is the ***denominator***.

Other well known fractions

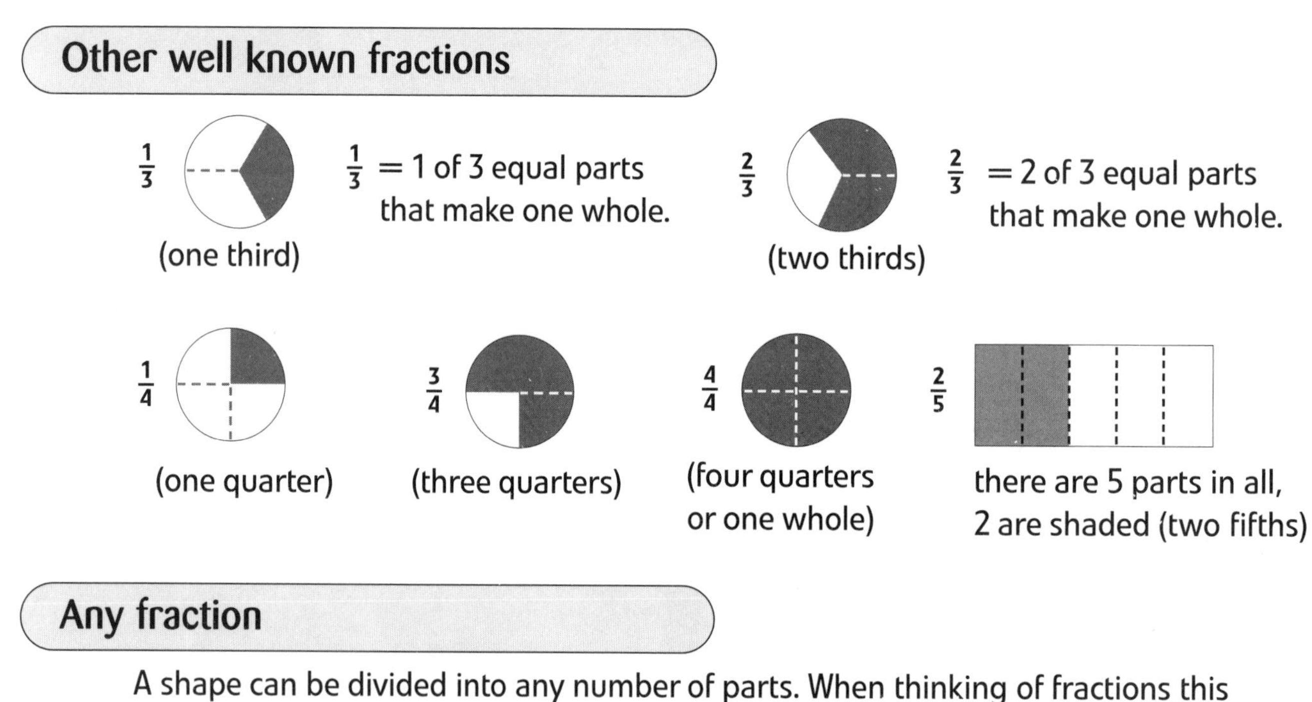

A shape can be divided into any number of parts. When thinking of fractions this number is the denominator.

E.g. The shape ÷ 12 equal parts = $\frac{}{12}$ (twelths)

E.g. 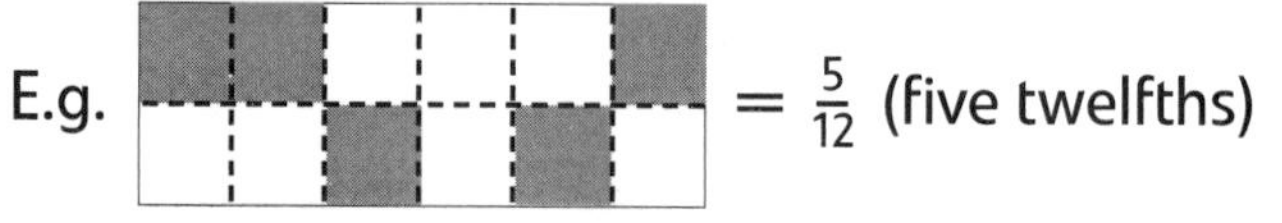 = $\frac{5}{12}$ (five twelfths)

The number of sections shaded then becomes the numerator.

Equivalent fraction

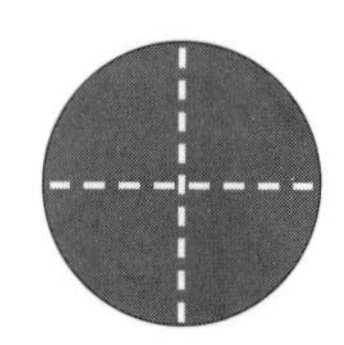

If a whole pizza was divided into 4 equal pieces and someone took 2 pieces, we could say that they had taken half of the pizza.

Another way of saying this would be that they had taken $\frac{2}{4}$. A $\frac{1}{2}$ is the same as $\frac{2}{4}$.

Likewise: $\frac{2}{3}$ = $\frac{4}{6}$

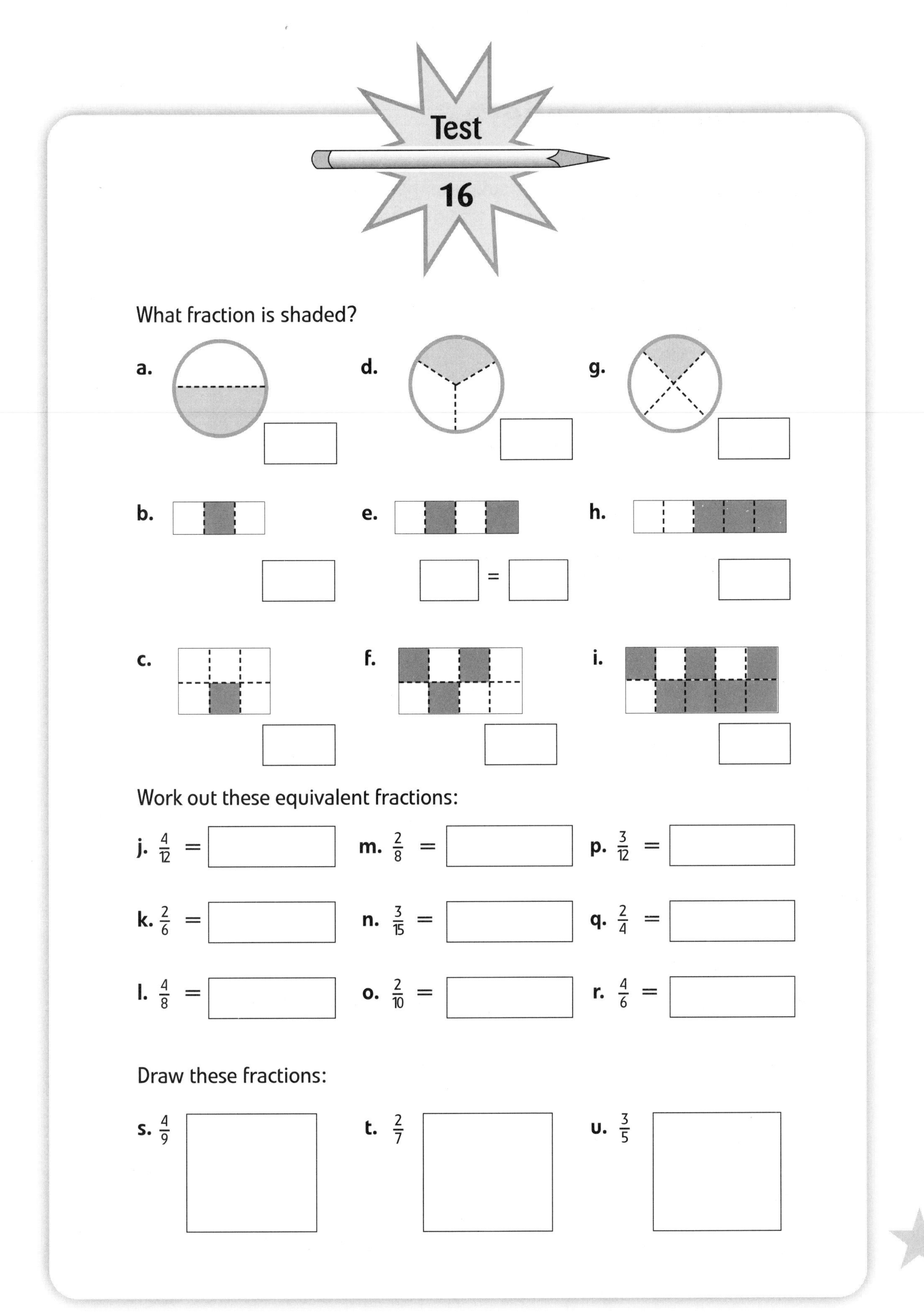

Test 16

What fraction is shaded?

a.

b.

c.

d.

e. =

f.

g.

h.

i.

Work out these equivalent fractions:

j. $\frac{4}{12}$ =

k. $\frac{2}{6}$ =

l. $\frac{4}{8}$ =

m. $\frac{2}{8}$ =

n. $\frac{3}{15}$ =

o. $\frac{2}{10}$ =

p. $\frac{3}{12}$ =

q. $\frac{2}{4}$ =

r. $\frac{4}{6}$ =

Draw these fractions:

s. $\frac{4}{9}$

t. $\frac{2}{7}$

u. $\frac{3}{5}$

Fractions of numbers

We know that in fractions, the denominator (bottom number) tells us how many there are in one whole, and the numerator (top number) tells us how many have been selected in this instance.

When we want to find fractions of numbers we have to treat the number as a whole and divide it up into the number of parts for the fraction.

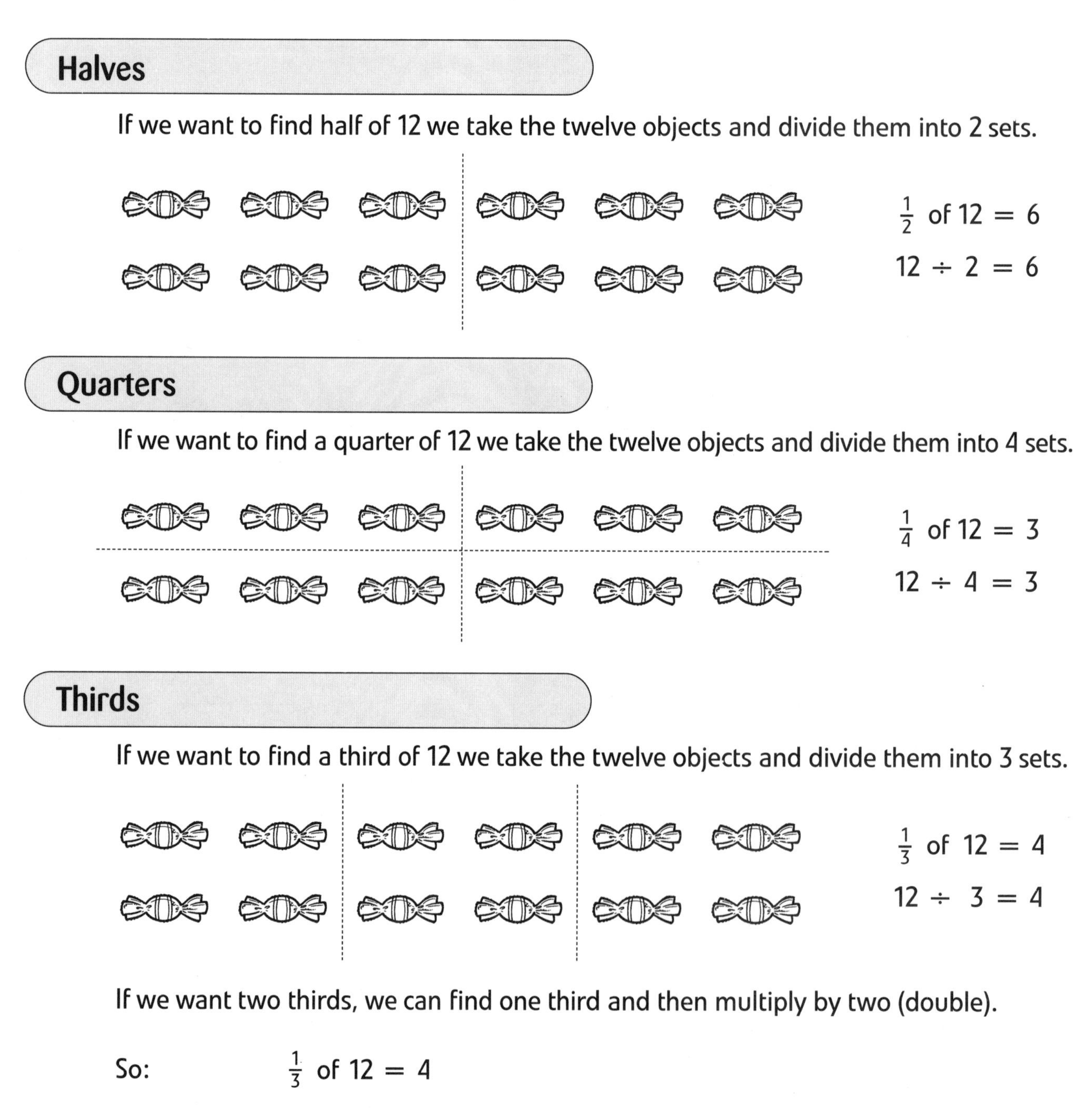

Halves

If we want to find half of 12 we take the twelve objects and divide them into 2 sets.

$\frac{1}{2}$ of $12 = 6$

$12 \div 2 = 6$

Quarters

If we want to find a quarter of 12 we take the twelve objects and divide them into 4 sets.

$\frac{1}{4}$ of $12 = 3$

$12 \div 4 = 3$

Thirds

If we want to find a third of 12 we take the twelve objects and divide them into 3 sets.

$\frac{1}{3}$ of $12 = 4$

$12 \div 3 = 4$

If we want two thirds, we can find one third and then multiply by two (double).

So: $\frac{1}{3}$ of $12 = 4$

Therefore: $\frac{2}{3}$ of 12 is $4 \times 2 = 8$

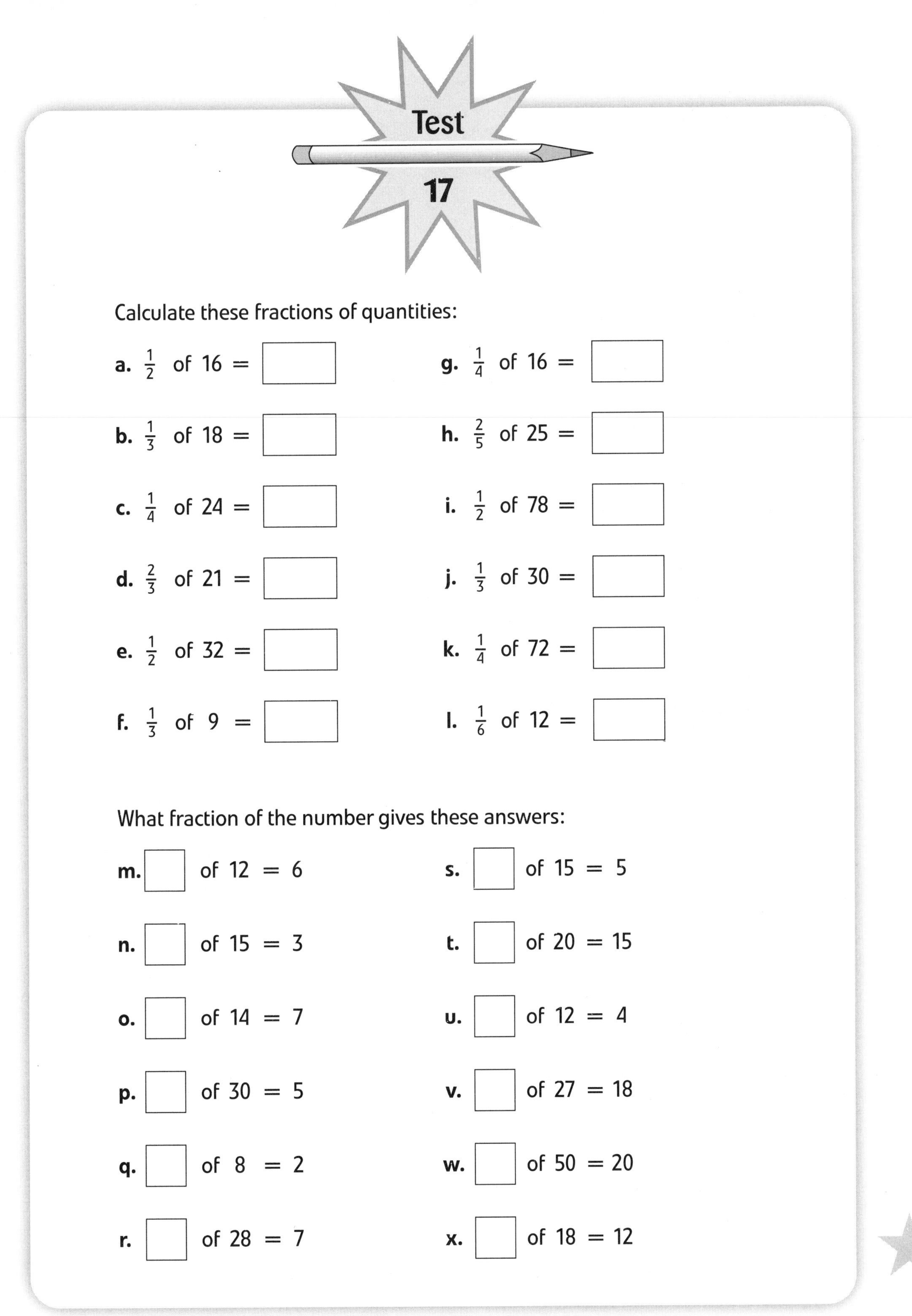

Test 17

Calculate these fractions of quantities:

a. $\frac{1}{2}$ of 16 = $\square$

b. $\frac{1}{3}$ of 18 = $\square$

c. $\frac{1}{4}$ of 24 = $\square$

d. $\frac{2}{3}$ of 21 = $\square$

e. $\frac{1}{2}$ of 32 = $\square$

f. $\frac{1}{3}$ of 9 = $\square$

g. $\frac{1}{4}$ of 16 = $\square$

h. $\frac{2}{5}$ of 25 = $\square$

i. $\frac{1}{2}$ of 78 = $\square$

j. $\frac{1}{3}$ of 30 = $\square$

k. $\frac{1}{4}$ of 72 = $\square$

l. $\frac{1}{6}$ of 12 = $\square$

What fraction of the number gives these answers:

m. $\square$ of 12 = 6

n. $\square$ of 15 = 3

o. $\square$ of 14 = 7

p. $\square$ of 30 = 5

q. $\square$ of 8 = 2

r. $\square$ of 28 = 7

s. $\square$ of 15 = 5

t. $\square$ of 20 = 15

u. $\square$ of 12 = 4

v. $\square$ of 27 = 18

w. $\square$ of 50 = 20

x. $\square$ of 18 = 12

Decimals

Place value

A ***decimal*** is also a part of something.

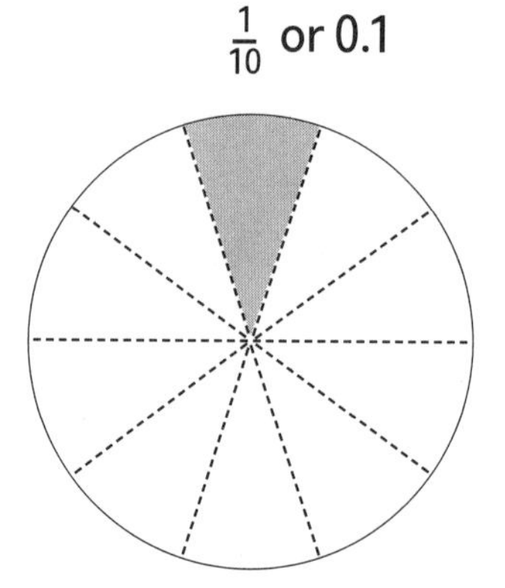

We start by looking at tenths. When a pizza is cut into 10 equal parts, each part is a tenth.

The decimal form for a tenth is 0.1 (zero point one).
For 2 tenths we write 0.2 (zero point two).
For 3 tenths we write 0.3 (zero point three) and so on.

Decimals also take account of hundredths. If something is cut into 100 equal pieces, each part is a hundredth.

The decimal for a hundredth is 0.01 (zero point zero one).
For 2 hundredths we write 0.02 (zero point zero two).
For 3 hundredths we write 0.03 (zero point zero three) and so on.

The law of place value operates here too. Just as we have Thousands, Hundreds, Tens, and Units for whole numbers, so for decimals we have Tenths, Hundredths and Thousandths. For example, look at the chart below:

Th	H	T	U	.	tenths	hundredths	thousandths	
		1	**2**	.	**3**			**Twelve point three** Twelve and three tenths
			1	.	**0**	**6**		**One point zero six** One and six hundredths
		3	**0**	.	**0**	**0**	**5**	**Thirty point zero zero five** Thirty and five thousandths

Ordering decimals

When ordering decimals, it is important to look at the place value of a digit. One tenth is bigger than one hundredth.
0.1 > 0.01

Similarly, one hundredth is bigger than one thousandth.
0.01 > 0.001

And 0.2 > 0.06 because two tenths is bigger than six hundredths.

Test 18

Place value

Write these words in figures:

a. Twelve point seven _____

b. Eight point nine _____

c. Thirty two point five _____

d. Thirty one point zero five _____

e. Twenty eight point zero two _____

f. Nineteen point one two _____

g. Seventeen point eight _____

h. Eighty point zero nine _____

Write these figures in words:

i. 12.4 ________________

j. 8.06 ________________

k. 41.6 ________________

l. 15.1 ________________

m. 9.7 ________________

n. 302.5 ________________

o. 31.12 ________________

p. 14.09 ________________

q. 98.11 ________________

r. 71.3 ________________

Ordering decimals

Circle the larger decimal in each of the following pairs:

s. 0.1 0.3

t. 0.3 0.25

u. 1.4 0.14

v. 3.8 3.09

w. 12.75 12.9

x. 14.8 14.19

Put these decimals in order, smallest first:

y. 3.75 3.7 3.5 3.62 3.2 3.9

____

Money

Decimal currency

In Great Britain, we have a ***decimal currency***, which is pounds and pence. There are 100 pennies in one pound. When we use the notation it looks like this:

25 pennies = 25p

3 pounds = £3.00

As there are 100 pennies in a pound, we can say that 1p is one hundredth of a pound. Remembering our place value of decimals, this can be written as 0.01 pounds or £0.01. Therefore, using notation:

25 pennies = 25p = £0.25

5 pennies = 5p = £0.05

125 pennies = 125p = £1.25 (remembering that there are 100 pennies in a pound)

When we are doing money calculations, we either convert the pounds to pennies or we convert the pennies to pounds. It is best to work in one way or the other to avoid confusion.

E.g. £2.00 + 47p can be expressed as:

200p + 47p = 247p

= £2.47

E.g. £2.00 + 47p can be expressed as:

£2.00 + £0.47 = £2.47

Test 19

Decimal currency

Using any combinations of coins, how could you make the following amounts?

a. 8p ______________________

b. 12p ______________________

c. 15p ______________________

d. 23p ______________________

e. 98p ______________________

Write these amounts using decimal notation:

f. 89p ____________

g. 98p ____________

h. 107p ____________

i. 310p ____________

j. 502p ____________

k. 205p ____________

If I had a £1.00 coin and needed to pay out these amounts, how much change would I have? Remember, £1.00 is the same as 100p.

l. 45p ____________

m. 80p ____________

n. 29p ____________

o. 79p ____________

p. 11p ____________

q. 84p ____________

How much have I spent?

r. 45p + 24p ____________

s. 32p + 76p ____________

t. 87p + 45p ____________

u. 129p + 32p ____________

v. 78p + 243p ____________

w. 24p + 61p ____________

Coordinates and compass points

Coordinates

Coordinates are used to locate points on a grid. They refer to the ***axes*** down the side and across the top or bottom. We usually use letters across the bottom and numbers up the side.

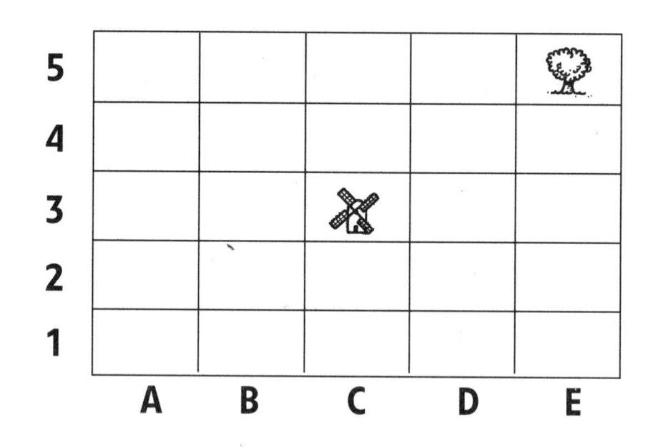

When reading coordinates, we need to remember a simple point – Go into the house before going up the stairs. **Go along the bottom axis before going up the vertical axis.** In the example above, to locate the windmill we must go along the bottom axis to C and up to 3. So, the coordinate of is C, 3.

Compass points

Also when locating objects we may use ***compass points***. A compass has four simple points: North, South, East, West.

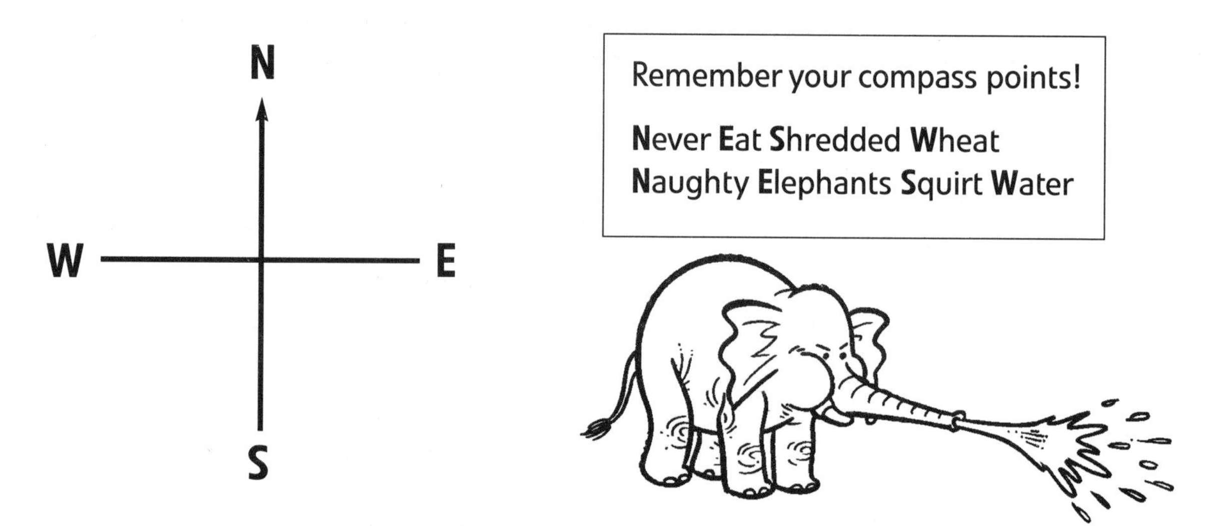

When using grids we can move across them using compass points. In the example above, from we can move East 2 and North 2 to find

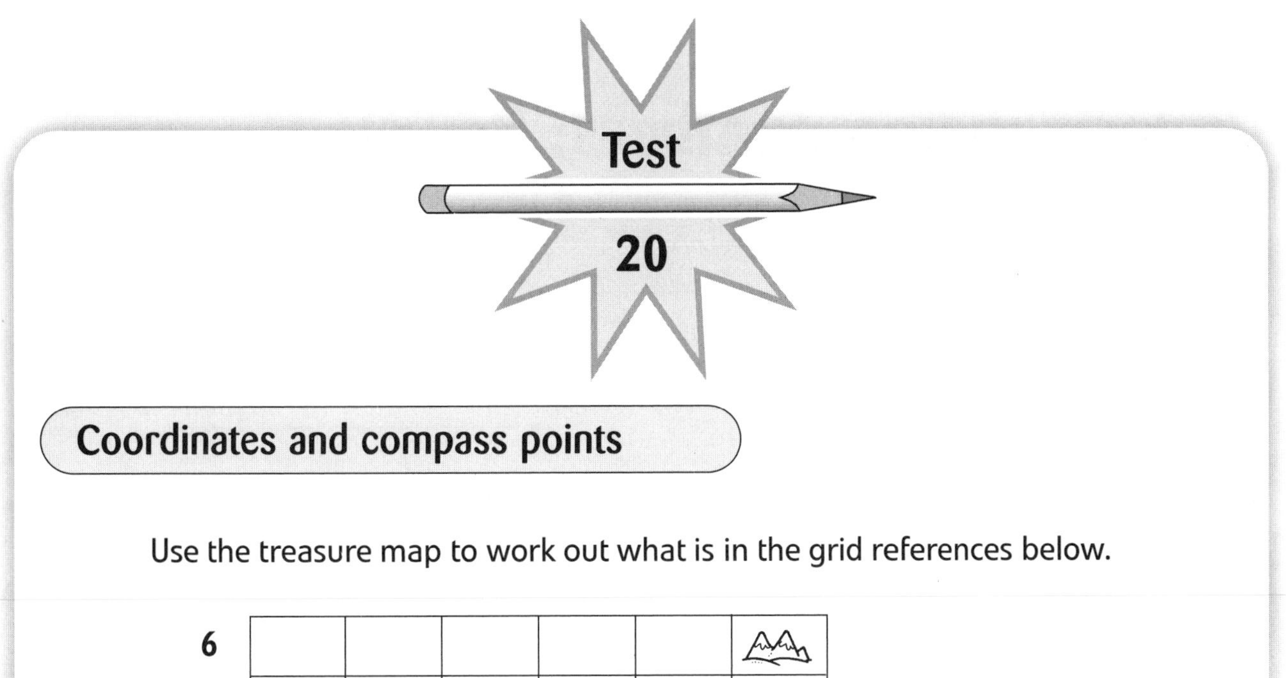

Coordinates and compass points

Use the treasure map to work out what is in the grid references below.

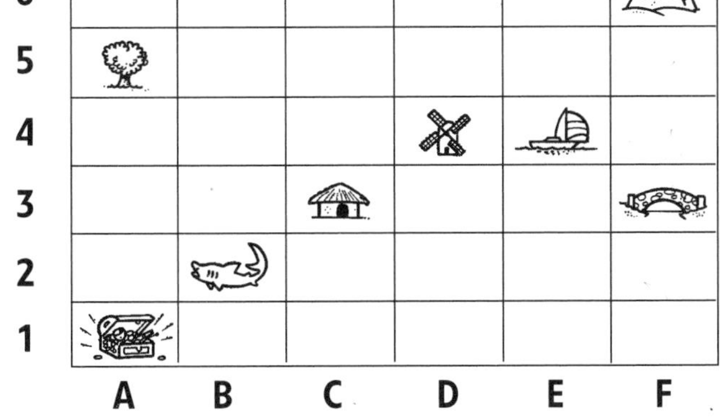

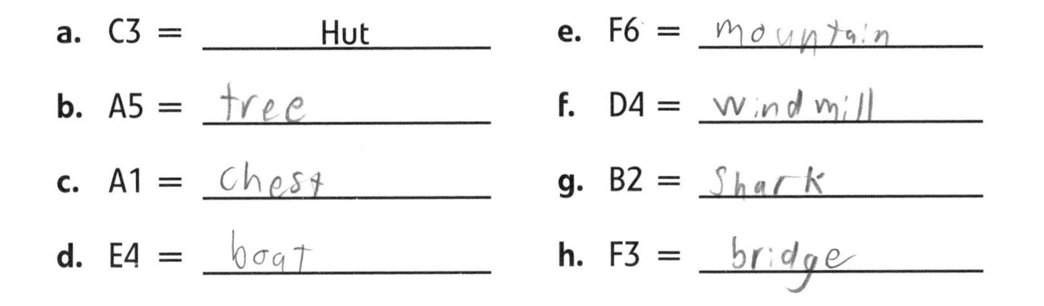

a. C3 = Hut

b. A5 = tree

c. A1 = chest

d. E4 = boat

e. F6 = mountain

f. D4 = windmill

g. B2 = Shark

h. F3 = bridge

Using the treasure map, follow the instructions below and work out which square you end up at.

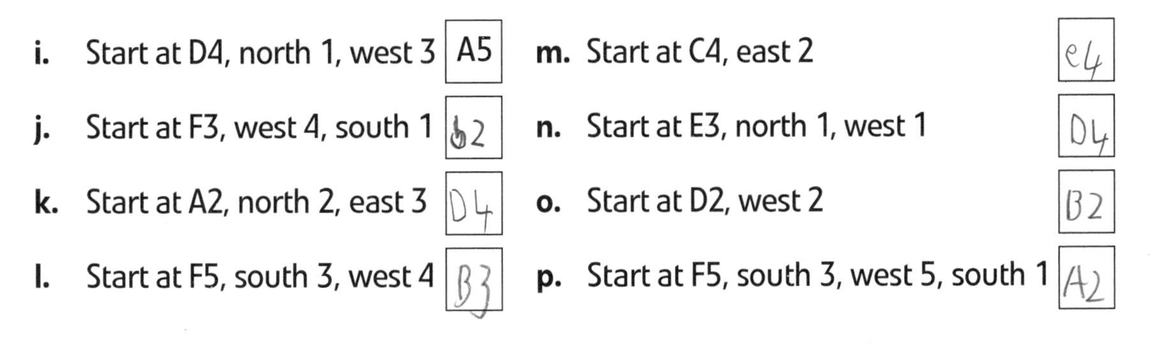

i. Start at D4, north 1, west 3 [A5]

j. Start at F3, west 4, south 1 [b2]

k. Start at A2, north 2, east 3 [D4]

l. Start at F5, south 3, west 4 [B3]

m. Start at C4, east 2 [e4]

n. Start at E3, north 1, west 1 [D4]

o. Start at D2, west 2 [B2]

p. Start at F5, south 3, west 5, south 1 [A2]

Understanding numbers: Revision

Place value

a. What is the digit 3 worth in 34? ____________

b. What is the digit 6 worth in 316? ____________

c. How many tens in 3425? ____________

d. How many hundreds in 6482? ____________

e. How many tens in 402? ____________

f. How many units in 3451? ____________

g. What is the largest number you can make from the digits 5, 6 and 8? ____________

h. What is the smallest number you can make from the digits 3, 1, 7 and 5? ____________

i. Write all the numbers you can make from the digits 1, 3 and 6.

________, ________, ________, ________, ________, ________

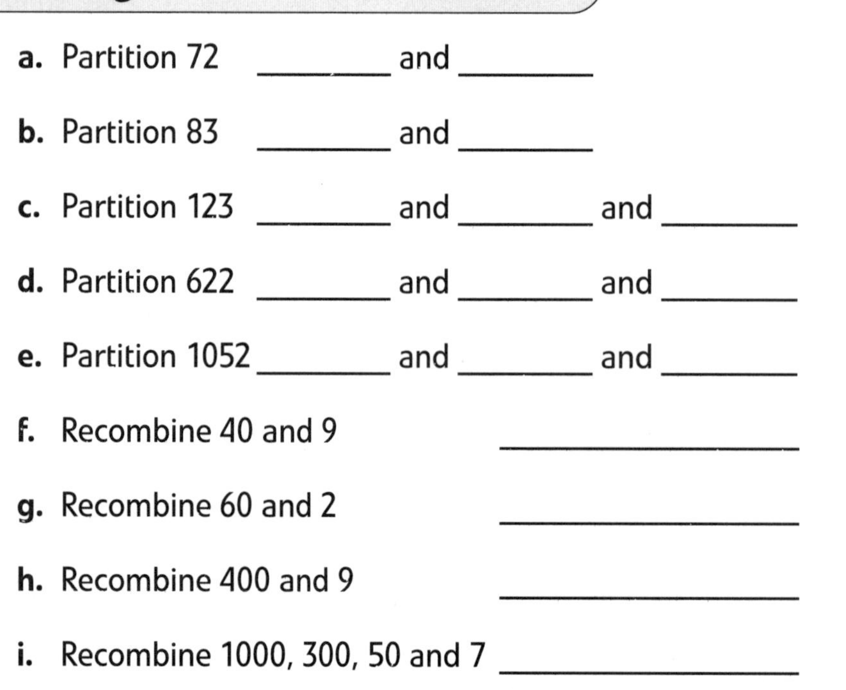

Partitioning

a. Partition 72 ________ and ________

b. Partition 83 ________ and ________

c. Partition 123 ________ and ________ and ________

d. Partition 622 ________ and ________ and ________

e. Partition 1052 ________ and ________ and ________

f. Recombine 40 and 9 ____________

g. Recombine 60 and 2 ____________

h. Recombine 400 and 9 ____________

i. Recombine 1000, 300, 50 and 7 ____________

Rounding, greater than and less than

a. 68 rounded to the nearest 10 is

b. 31 rounded to the nearest 10 is

c. 75 rounded to the nearest 10 is

d. 83 rounded to the nearest 10 is

e. 99 rounded to the nearest 10 is

f. 345 rounded to the nearest 10 is

g. 868 rounded to the nearest 10 is

h. 1071 rounded to the nearest 10 is

i. Is 36 greater than 42? YES/NO

j. Is 96 greater than 92? YES/NO

k. Is 83 less than 74? YES/NO

l. Is 29 less than 39? YES/NO

m. Is $39 > 29$? YES/NO

n. Is $75 < 22$? YES/NO

o. Is $105 > 102$? YES/NO

p. Is $454 < 545$? YES/NO

Number pairs that total 10 and 20

a. 6 + ___ = 10

b. 1 + ___ = 10

c. ___ + 3 = 10

d. 10 + ___ = 10

e. 9 + ___ = 10

f. 2 + ___ = 10

g. ___ + 5 = 10

h. 17 + ___ = 20

i. 5 + ___ = 20

j. ___ + 8 = 20

k. 20 - ___ = 16

l. 20 - ___ = 9

m. 20 - ___ = 12

n. 20 = ___ + 4

o. 20 = ___ + 14

p. 20 = 5 + ___

Understanding numbers: Revision

Addition using partitioning

a. 16 + 22 = ______

b. 18 + 31 = ______

c. 17 + 13 = ______

d. 27 + 22 = ______

e. 34 + 24 = ______

f. 45 + 16 = ______

g. 81 + 36 = ______

h. 54 + 33 = ______

i. 72 + 35 = ______

j. 134 + 44 = ______

k. 155 + 132 = ______

l. 245 + 124 = ______

Show your workings. (You can continue on a separate sheet of paper if you need to.)

Subtraction using partitioning

a. 67 - 23 = ______

b. 88 - 54 = ______

c. 42 - 22 = ______

d. 67 - 34 = ______

e. 95 - 54 = ______

f. 139 - 113 = ______

Subtraction using a number line

a. 84 - 62 = ______

b. 92 - 67 = ______

c. 54 - 37 = ______

d. 146 - 78 = ______

e. 174 - 138 = ______

f. 130 - 16 = ______

Show your workings.

Understanding numbers: Revision

Counting on in tens and units using a number line

a. 67 + 36 =

b. 23 + 57 =

c. 38 + 45 =

d. 134 + 67 =

e. 156 + 27 =

f. 216 + 74 =

g. 546 + 38 =

Doubling and halving

a. Double 6 = ______

b. Double 5 = ______

c. Double 9 = ______

d. Double 12 = ______

e. Double 32 = ______

f. Double 40 = ______

g. Double 65 = ______

h. Double 124 = ______

i. 58 x 2 = ______

j. 63 x 2 = ______

k. Double £8.00 = ______

l. Double 18cm = ______

m. 6 x 4 = ______

n. 12 x 4 = ______

o. 24 x 4 = ______

p. Halve 6 = ______

q. Halve 10 = ______

r. Halve 22 = ______

s. Halve 48 = ______

t. Halve 96 = ______

u. Halve 100 = ______

v. Halve 450 = ______

w. Halve £5.00 = ______

x. Halve 38cm = ______

Multiplication tables

a. 6 x 3 = ______

b. 7 x 4 = ______

c. 3 x 3 = ______

d. 4 x 2 = ______

e. 7 x 5 = ______

f. 10 x 3 = ______

g. 4 x 5 = ______

h. 6 x 5 = ______

Complete these number patterns using your tables knowledge:

i. 6, 9, 12, ___, ___, ___

j. 55, 50, 45, ___, ___, ___

k. 8, 10, 12, ___, ___, ___

l. 10, 20, 30, ___, ___, ___

Understanding numbers: Revision

Inverse operations

Use each of the number families below to write up to four number sentences.

E.g. 4, 8 and 12

$4 + 8 = 12$ $8 + 4 = 12$ $12 - 4 = 8$ $12 - 8 = 4$

a. 7, 12, 5 ____________________________

b. 4, 1, 3 ____________________________

c. 6, 4, 24 ____________________________

d. 5, 3, 15 ____________________________

e. 10, 10, 100 ____________________________

f. 6, 3, 9 ____________________________

g. 12, 12, 24 ____________________________

h. 2, 8, 16 ____________________________

i. 14, 16, 30 ____________________________

j. 100, 20, 80 ____________________________

Multiplication with larger numbers

a. 16 x 5 = ________

b. 18 x 4 = ________

c. 21 x 3 = ________

d. 45 x 5 = ________

e. 63 x 4 = ________

f. 125 x 3 = ________

g. 161 x 5 = ________

h. 185 x 2 = ________

i. 241 x 4 = ________

j. 312 x 3 = ________

k. 450 x 3 = ________

Division

a. 27 ÷ 3 = ________

b. 40 ÷ 10 = ________

c. 18 ÷ 2 = ________

d. 50 ÷ 5 = ________

e. 16 ÷ 4 = ________

f. 20 ÷ 5 = ________

g. 48 ÷ 2 = ________

h. 100 ÷ 4 = ________

i. 400 ÷ 4 = ________

j. 22 ÷ 2 = ________

k. 32 ÷ 4 = ________

l. 60 ÷ 5 = ________

m. 30 ÷ 3 = ________

n. 45 ÷ 5 = ________

o. 80 ÷ 2 = ________

p. 35 ÷ 5 = ________

Multiplying and dividing by 10 and 100

a. 6 x 10 = ________

b. 12 x 10 = ________

c. 42 x 10 = ________

d. 81 x 10 = ________

e. 457 x 10 = ________

f. 346 x 10 = ________

g. 9 x 100 = ________

h. 16 x 100 = ________

i. 28 x 100 = ________

j. 453 x 100 = ________

k. 678 x 100 = ________

l. 70 ÷ 10 = ________

m. 90 ÷ 10 = ________

n. 120 ÷ 10 = ________

o. 220 ÷ 10 = ________

p. 100 ÷ 100 = ________

q. 1600 ÷ 100 = ________

r. 8400 ÷ 100 = ________

s. 10400 ÷ 100= ________

t. 4500 people are going to a concert. Each coach holds 100 people. How many coaches are needed to take everyone to the concert? ________

Understanding numbers: Revision

Fabulous facts

a. The factors of 6 are ____, ____, ____, ____

b. The factors of 12 are ____, ____, ____, ____, ____, ____

c. Write two odd numbers that are less than 10 ____, ____

d. Write two even numbers between 26 and 36 ____, ____

e. Continue the sequence: 21, 24, 27, 30, ____, ____, ____

f. Continue the sequence: 56, 52, 48, 44, ____, ____, ____

Fractions of numbers

a. $\frac{1}{2}$ of 12 = ________

b. $\frac{1}{5}$ of 25 = ________

c. $\frac{1}{3}$ of 30 = ________

d. $\frac{1}{3}$ of 18 = ________

e. $\frac{1}{6}$ of 12 = ________

f. $\frac{1}{4}$ of 20 = ________

Write the fraction:

g. ________ of 10 = 5

h. ________ of 16 = 4

i. ________ of 20 = 5

j. ________ of 100 = 50

Decimals

a. What is the value of the digit 7 in 7.12? ____________

b. What is the value of the digit 3 in 6.31? ____________

c. What is the value of the digit 9 in 0.19? ____________

Put these numbers in order, starting with the smallest:

d. 0.12, 0.2, 0.6, 0.05 ____, ____, ____, ____

e. 12.5, 12.7, 12.09, 12.8 ____, ____, ____, ____

Money

Write these amounts using decimal notation:

a. 89p ________

b. 345p ________

c. 230p ________

d. 208p ________

e. 1735p ________

How many pennies are in:

f. £1.70 ________

g. £1.90 ________

h. £0.76 ________

i. £0.07 ________

j. £12.34 ________

Coordinates

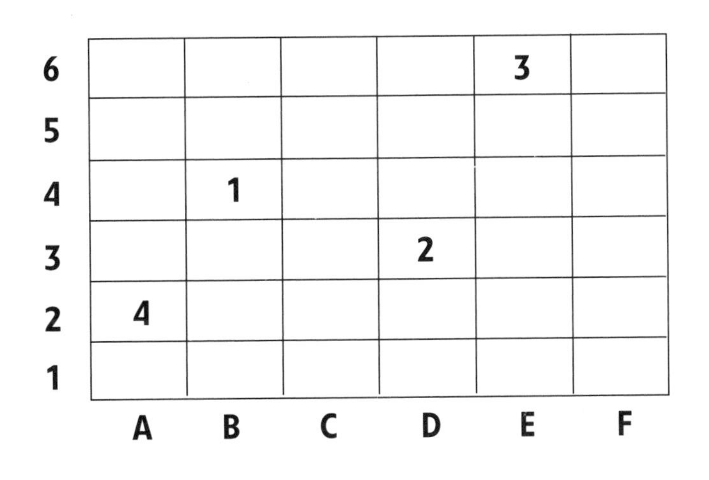

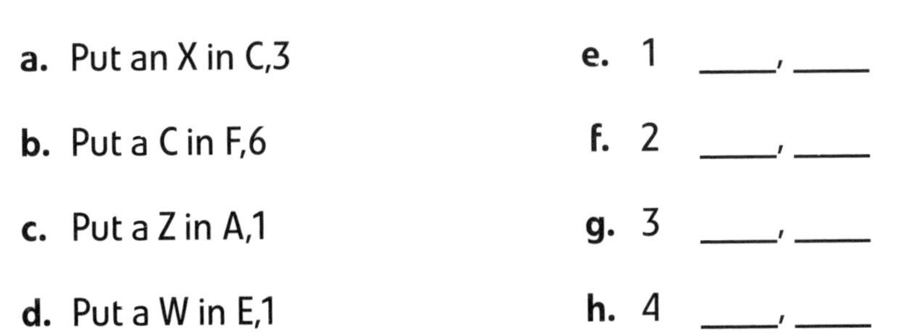

a. Put an X in C,3

b. Put a C in F,6

c. Put a Z in A,1

d. Put a W in E,1

Where are these numbers?

e. 1 ___, ___

f. 2 ___, ___

g. 3 ___, ___

h. 4 ___, ___

Venn diagrams

A ***Venn diagram*** is a way in which we can sort a set of data.

Sorting by one criterion

We can start by sorting the data by **one criterion.** We simply see if each item within the set of data satisfies this criterion.

E.g. The data chosen is a set of clothes:

Bikini	Boots
Shorts	Scarf
Woolly hat	Jumper
T-shirt	Flip flops
Sandals	Sun-hat

The criterion is 'suitable for a hot day'.

Having decided whether each item of clothing is suitable for a hot day or not we can then complete the Venn diagram: those that are suitable go ***inside*** the circle, those that are not go ***outside*** the circle.

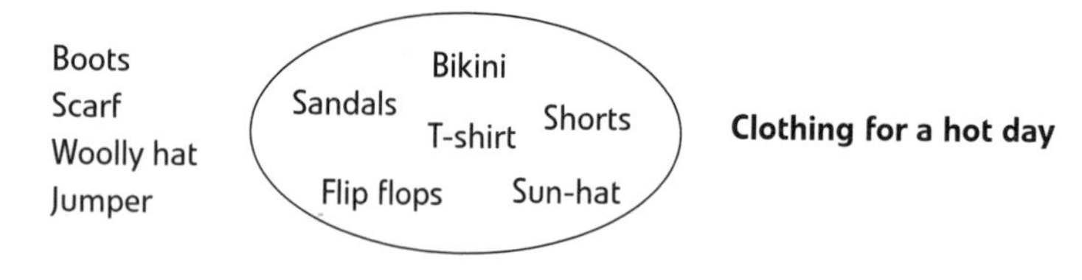

Sorting by two criteria

Having sorted by one criterion, we can then introduce a **second criterion**. Let's make our second criterion, 'suitable to be worn on the feet'. This time we have to sort each piece of data by two criteria. If the item satisfies the criterion, it must be placed in that circle. However, if the item satisfies both criteria, do we have a problem? Not at all!

A Venn diagram for two criteria looks like this:

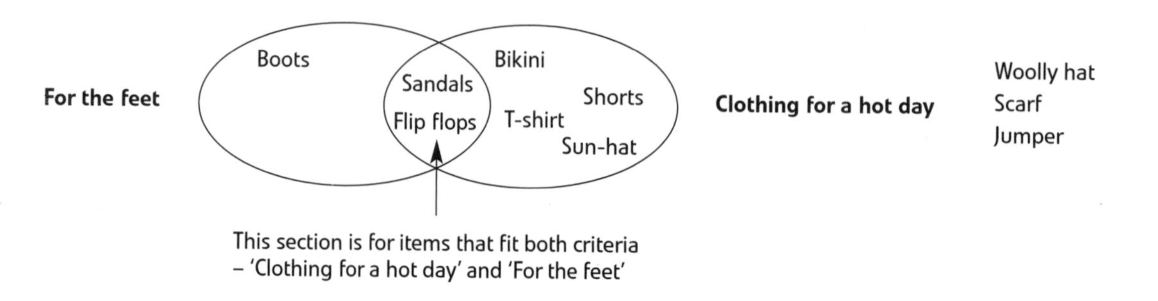

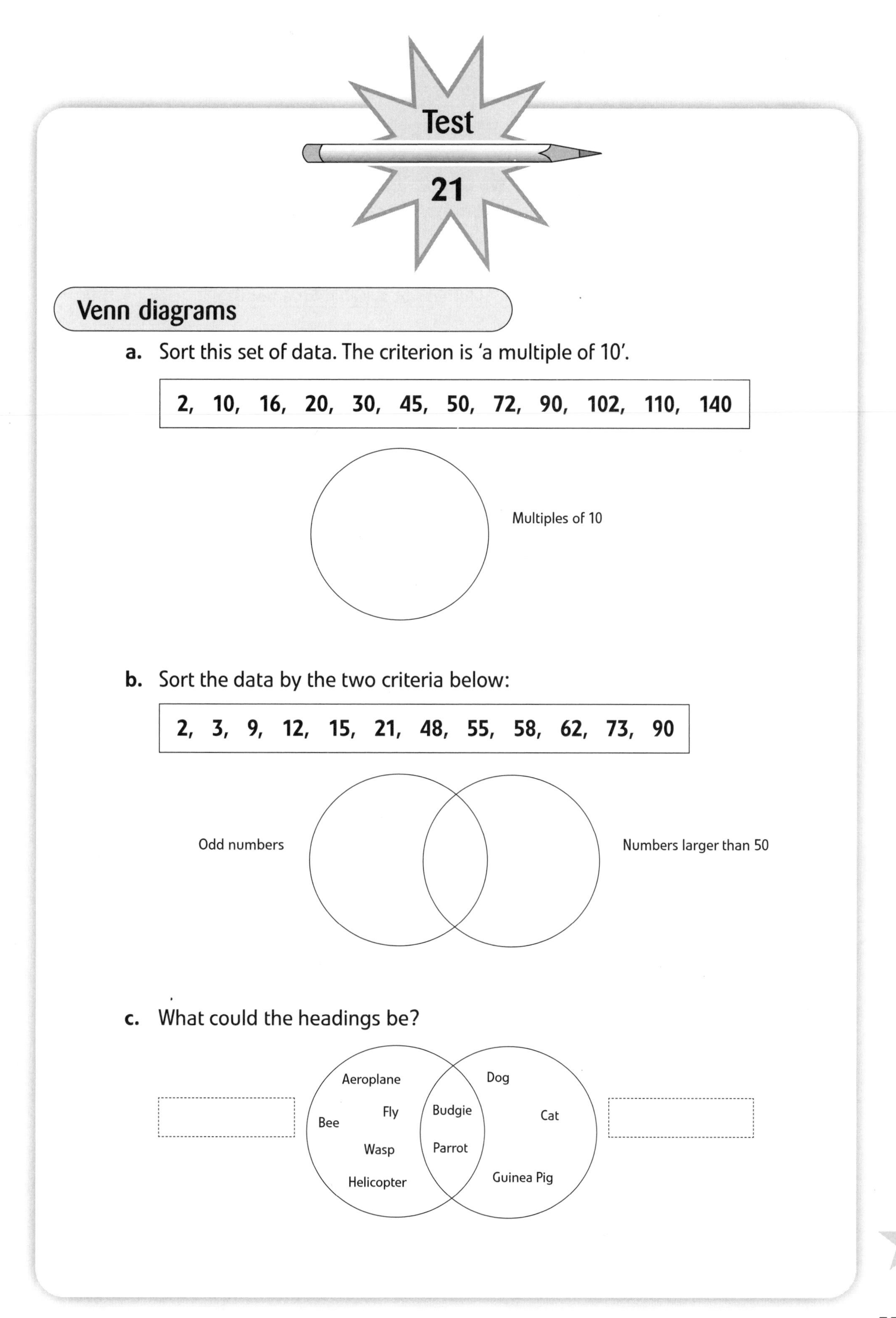

Test 21

Venn diagrams

a. Sort this set of data. The criterion is 'a multiple of 10'.

2, 10, 16, 20, 30, 45, 50, 72, 90, 102, 110, 140

Multiples of 10

b. Sort the data by the two criteria below:

2, 3, 9, 12, 15, 21, 48, 55, 58, 62, 73, 90

Odd numbers

Numbers larger than 50

c. What could the headings be?

Carroll diagrams

A ***Carroll diagram*** is another tool we can use for sorting a set of data. It is just like completing a table. As with Venn diagrams, we can sort firstly by one criterion. We just record the results in a different way:

Clothes suitable for a hot day	Clothes not suitable for a hot day
Bikini	Scarf
Sun-hat	Woolly hat
Shorts	Jumper
T-shirt	Boots
Sandals	
Flip flops	

When we sort by two criteria, we have to take account of this in our table. We must now look very carefully at the headings of the columns **and** the rows before we choose which box to write in:

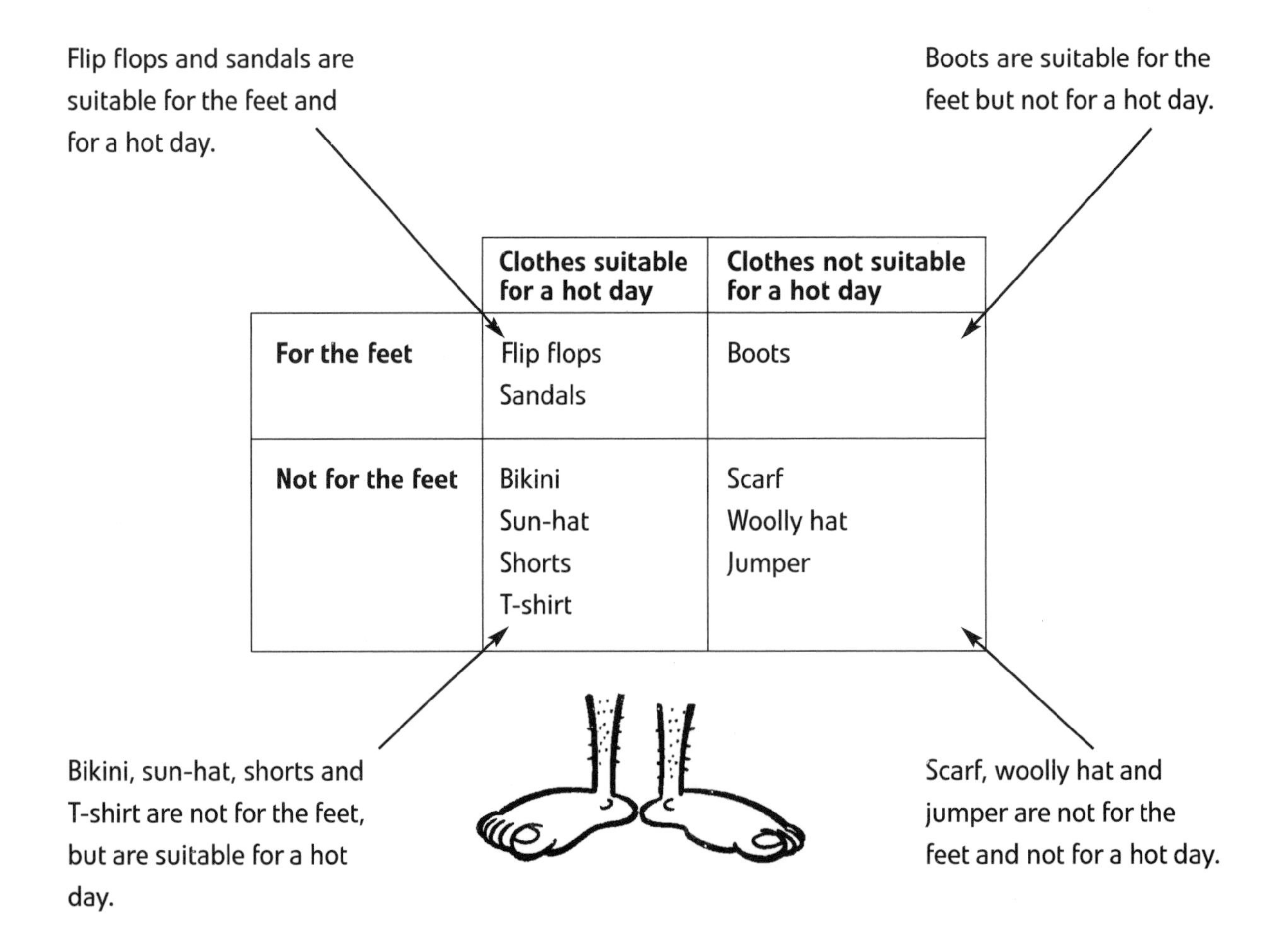

	Clothes suitable for a hot day	Clothes not suitable for a hot day
For the feet	Flip flops Sandals	Boots
Not for the feet	Bikini Sun-hat Shorts T-shirt	Scarf Woolly hat Jumper

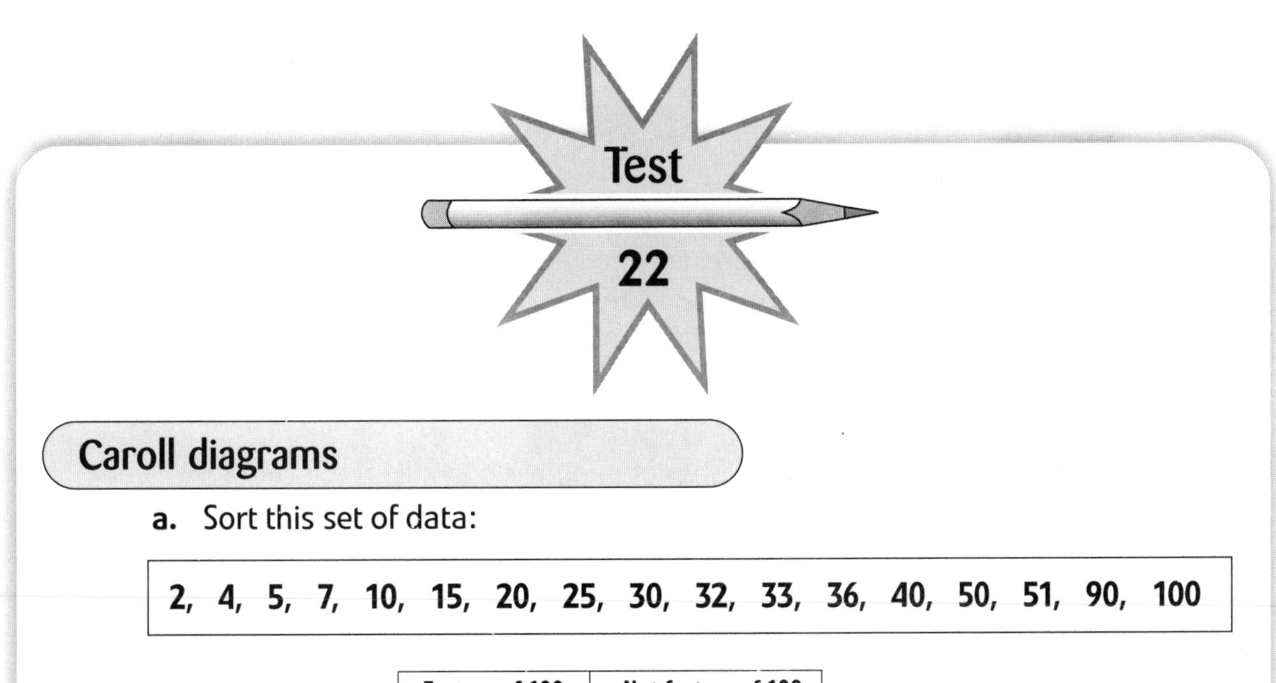

Caroll diagrams

a. Sort this set of data:

2, 4, 5, 7, 10, 15, 20, 25, 30, 32, 33, 36, 40, 50, 51, 90, 100

Factors of 100	Not factors of 100

b. Now sort the same data into this Carroll diagram with extra criteria:

	Factors of 100	Not factors of 100
Odd numbers		
Not odd numbers		

c. What could the headings be?

	Sausages Bacon	Pork chop Chicken kiev Mince beef Corned beef
	Egg Tomatoes Cereal Mushrooms Milk Bread Jam	Cake Pasta Pizza

Bar charts

Bar charts are another way of representing data. This time, blocks are used to build a tower for each group of data. We need to have a scale to be able to read what these blocks are. The scale might count in 1s, 2s, 5s or 10s – it is important to look at what each line represents.

This is a bar chart showing the number of people who walked to school this week.

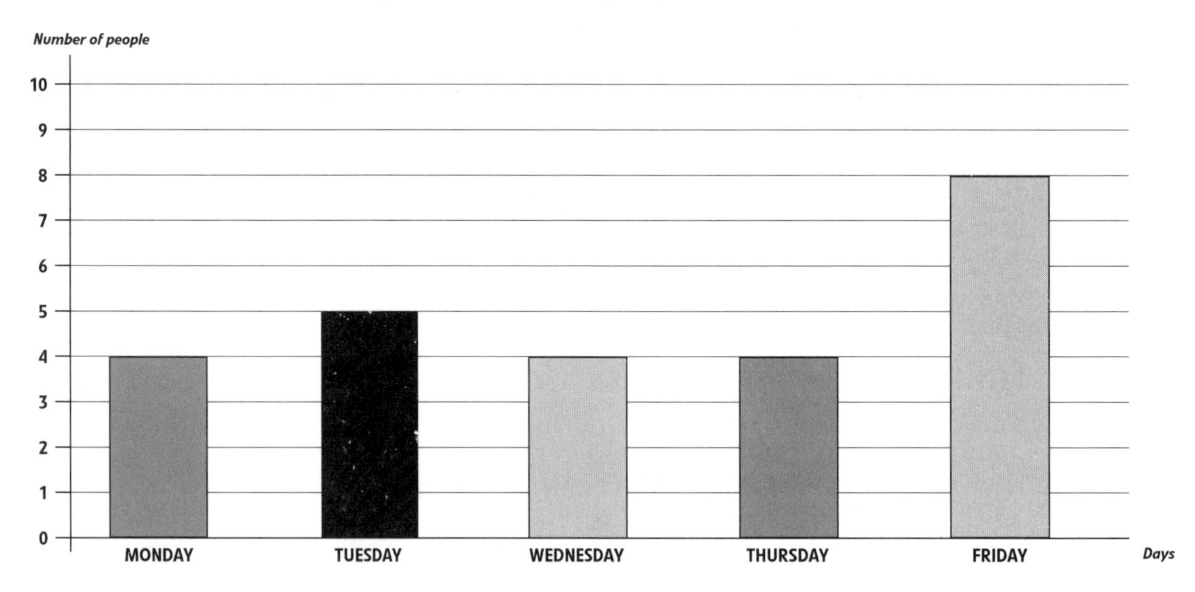

We can read this information to see that:

★ Monday	4 people walked to school
★ Tuesday	5 people walked to school
★ Wednesday	4 people walked to school
★ Thursday	4 people walked to school
★ Friday	8 people walked to school

We can also see clearly the answers to these questions:

On which day did most people walk to school?
Friday

On which days did the least number of people walk to school?
Monday, Wednesday, Thursday

When did 5 people walk to school?
Tuesday

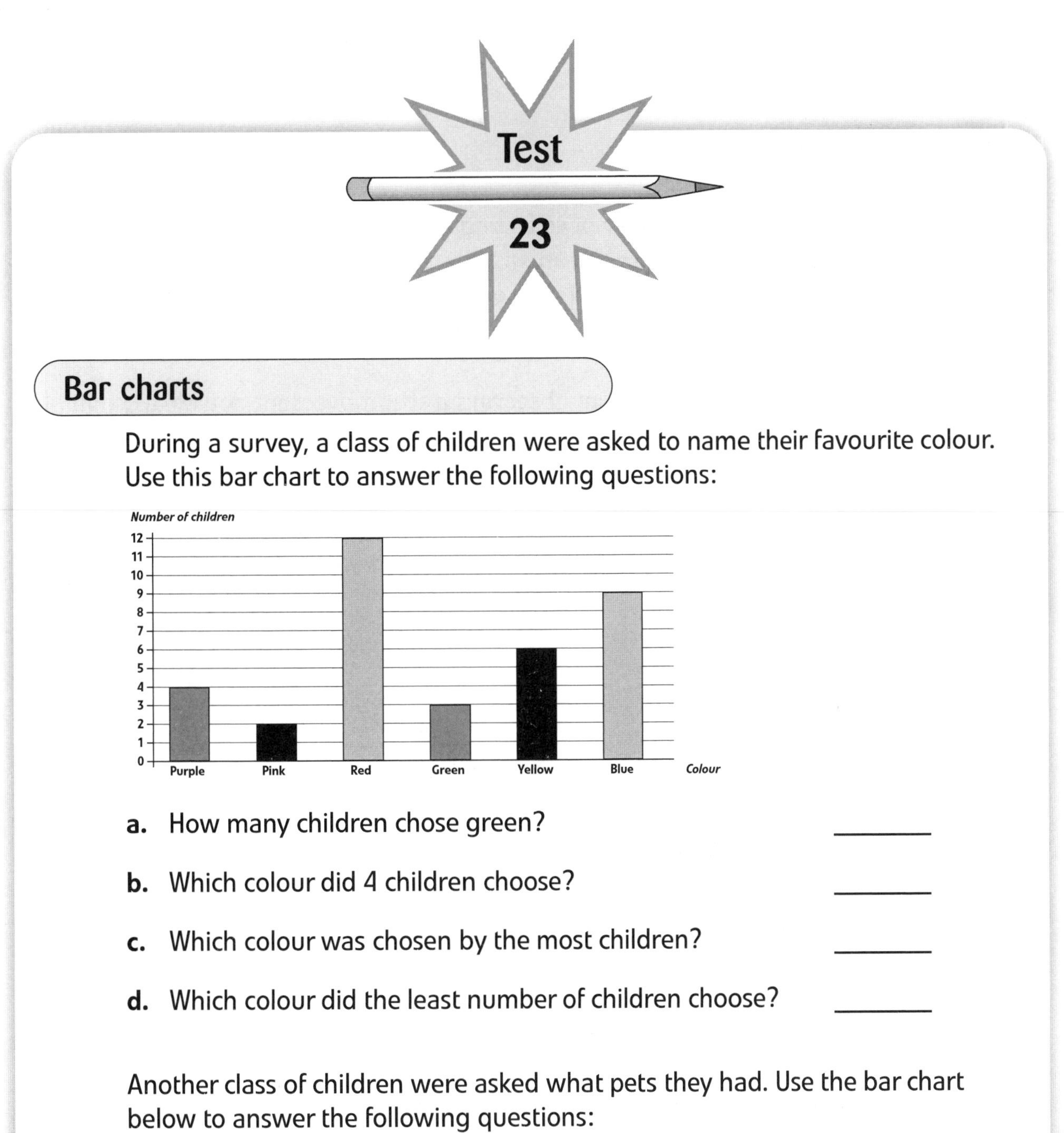

Test 23

Bar charts

During a survey, a class of children were asked to name their favourite colour. Use this bar chart to answer the following questions:

a. How many children chose green? ________

b. Which colour did 4 children choose? ________

c. Which colour was chosen by the most children? ________

d. Which colour did the least number of children choose? ________

Another class of children were asked what pets they had. Use the bar chart below to answer the following questions:

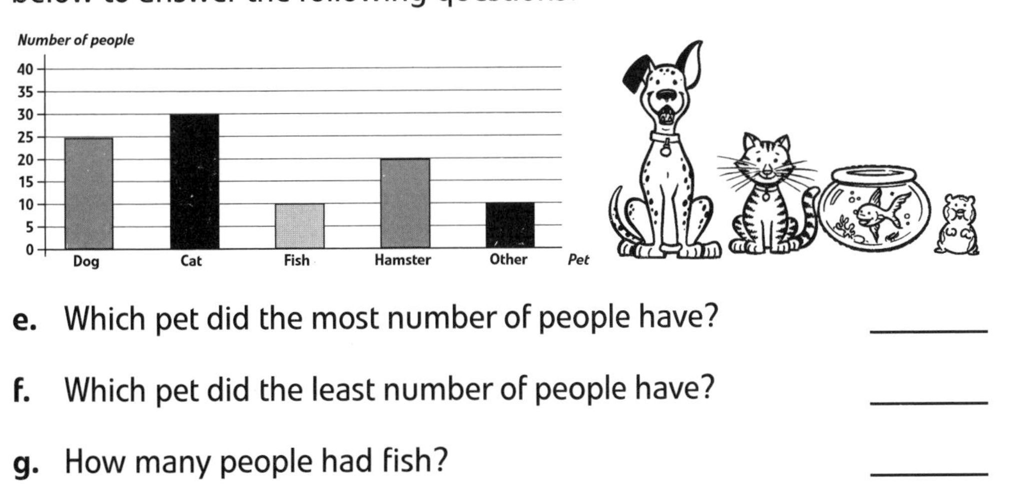

e. Which pet did the most number of people have? ________

f. Which pet did the least number of people have? ________

g. How many people had fish? ________

h. How many people had dogs? ________

Tally charts

A ***tally chart*** is an alternative way of collecting data. This time we use marks, known as tallies, for each item noted. This is an easier way of collecting a set of data where the sample is not a specific number, for example a 30-minute traffic survey along the main road. Each vehicle is tallied and then the tally is totalled at the end of the survey.

For example: 30 minutes were spent observing traffic movement outside a school. The results are listed in the tally below.

Vehicle	Tally	Total
Car	卌 卌 卌 卌 卌 卌 ||||	34
Van	卌 |	6
Bus	||||	4
Lorry	卌 ||	7
Bike	||||	4

From this tally chart, we can see that:

★ 34 cars went past school
★ 6 vans went past school
★ 4 buses went past school
★ 7 lorries went past school
★ 4 bikes went past school

We can also use the data from tally charts to draw simple bar charts or pictograms. When we are drawing these, we need to look at the data to see what the highest number is (in this case 34) and how many categories there are (in this case 5). We can then think about the scale we would like the vertical axis to use (in this case a scale of 5 would be a sensible choice). Once we have made these decisions, we can draw and label the axes, and then draw each block as tall as it needs to be.

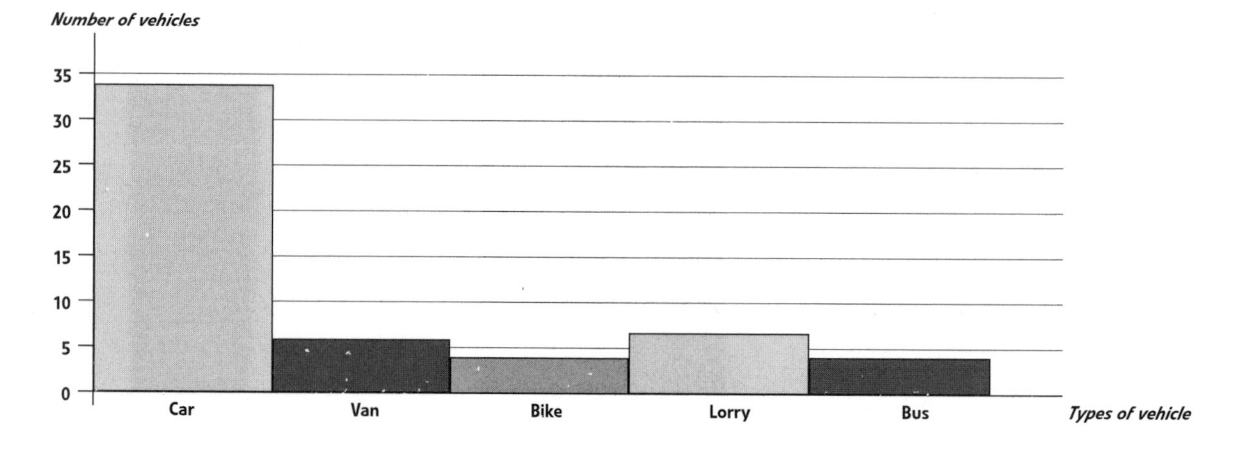

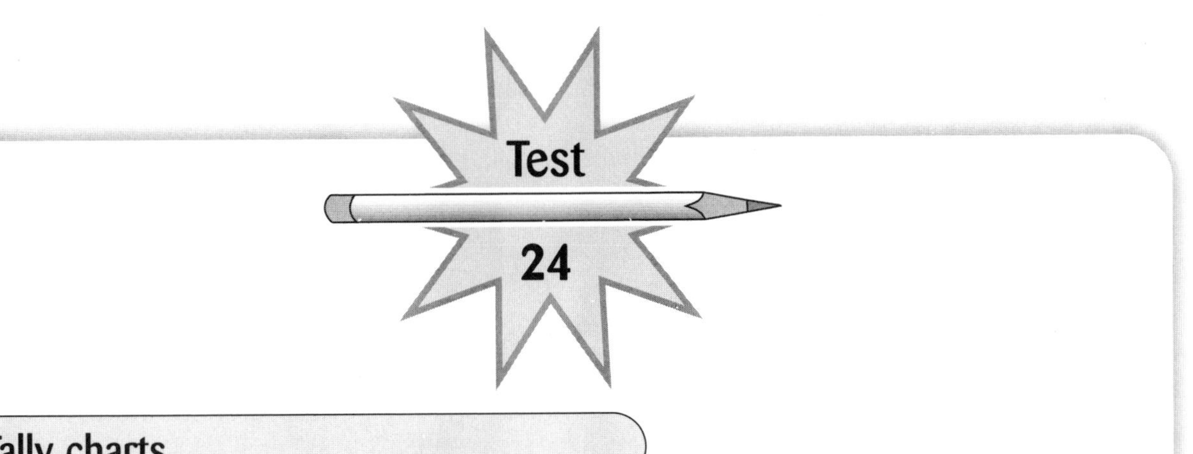

Tally charts

As part of a survey of bus passengers, people were asked which of the following age groups they fell into: under 25, 26 to 39, 40 to 59, or 60+. The results were 28, 12, 18, and 33 respectively.

Complete this tally chart to represent this information and then use it to complete the bar chart.

a. Tally chart

Age of passengers	Tally	Total
Under 25	~~IIII~~ ~~IIII~~ ~~IIII~~ ~~IIII~~ ~~IIII~~ III	28
26-39		
40-59		
60+		

b. Bar chart

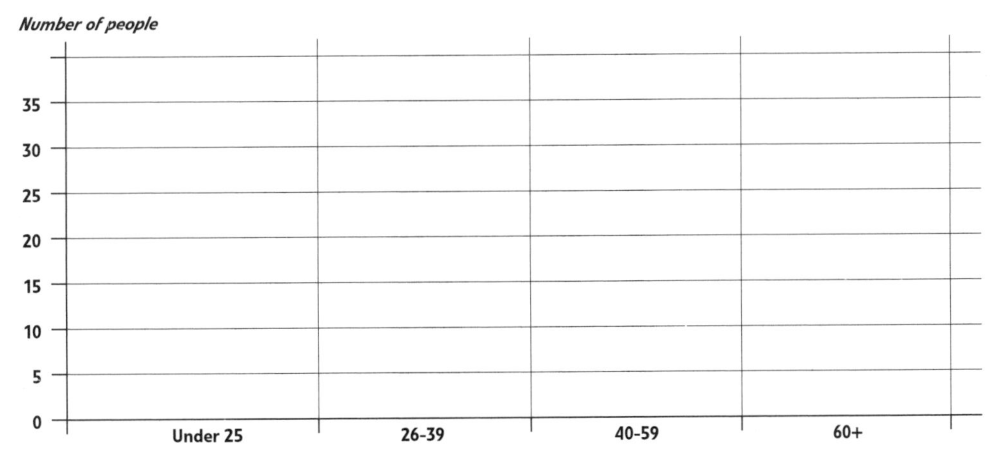

Frequency tables

Frequency tables

A ***frequency table*** is another simple way of collecting data. The simplest way of collecting data is to ask a viewpoint of a group of people and allow them to vote using a show of hands. The number of hands shown is then totalled and recorded in a table.

For example: 30 children were asked what their favourite playtime snack was. They were given the following choices: crisps, fruit, chocolate, biscuits or sweets. Their responses are listed in the table below.

Favourite playtime snack	Number of children
Crisps	12
Fruit	11
Chocolate	4
Biscuits	1
Sweets	2

From this frequency table, we can see that:

★ 12 children chose crisps
★ 11 children chose fruit
★ 4 children chose chocolate
★ 1 child chose biscuits
★ 2 children chose sweets

We can also use the data from frequency tables to draw simple bar charts or pictograms. As was mentioned before, when we are drawing these, we need to look at the data to see what the highest number is (in this case 12) and how many categories there are (in this case 5).

We can then think about the scale we would like the vertical axis to use (in this case a scale of 2 would be a sensible choice). Once we have made these decisions, we can draw and label the axes, and then draw each block, as tall as it needs to be.

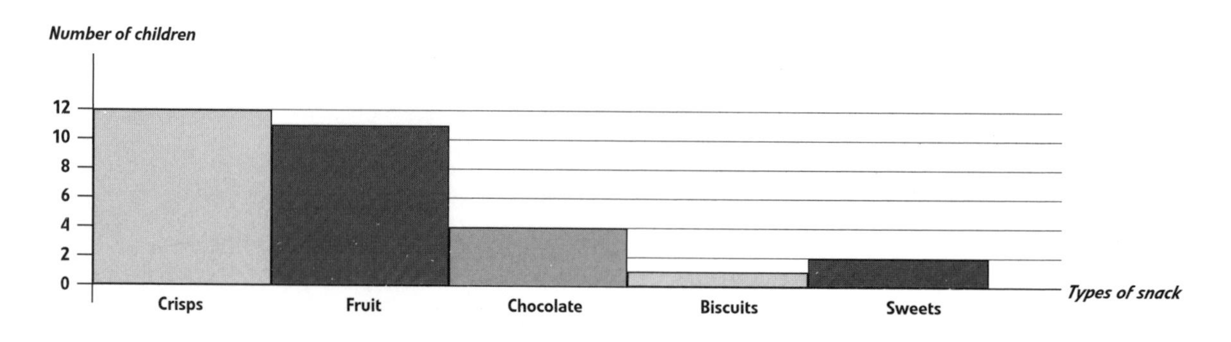

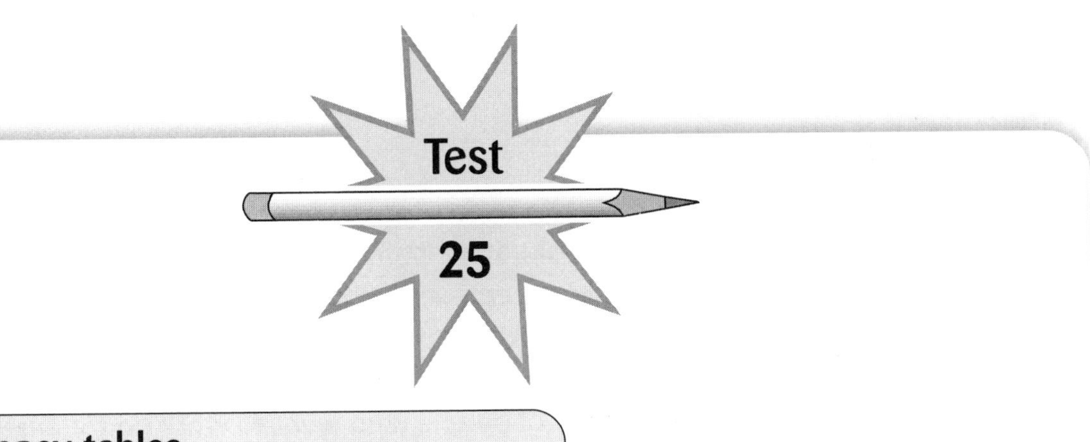

Frequency tables

The children in Class 3 were talking about the number of letters in their names. Their names either had 3 letters, 4 letters, 5 letters or 6+ letters.

Here are the children's names. Use the information to complete the frequency table and then the bar chart:

David	John	Alex	Guy	Paul	Rob
Simon	Stephen	Tom	Harry	James	Nick
Sarah	Jane	Helen	Shana	Jill	Kim
Grace	Jessica	Annie	Sophie	Zoe	Karen

a. Frequency table

Letters in name	Number of children
3 letters	
4 letters	
5 letters	
6+ letters	

b. Bar chart

Number of children

12
10
8
6
4
2
0

3 letters 4 letters 5 letters 6+ letters

Letters in name

Pictograms

Pictograms are a representation of data. Pictures are used for each item of data. Sometimes a picture can be used to represent a group of data. We might also see half a picture, meaning half the group of data.

This pictogram shows the number of people who went to work on the bus this week.

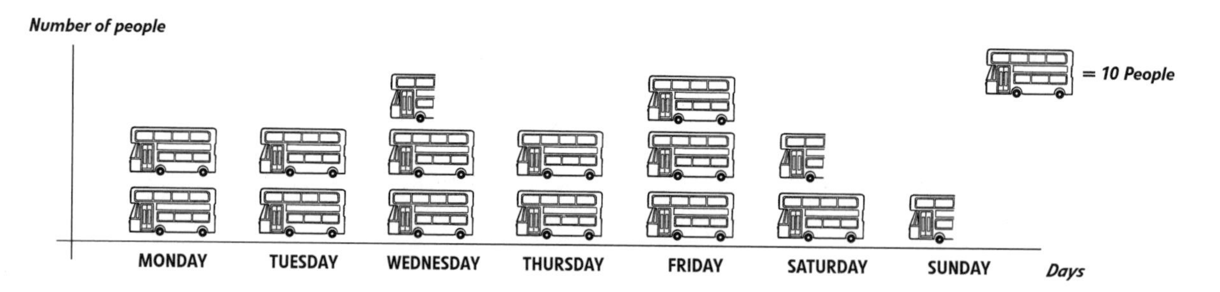

We can read the information to see that:

★ Monday $10 \times 2 = 20$ people went to work on the bus

★ Tuesday $10 \times 2 = 20$ people went to work on the bus

★ Wednesday $10 \times 2 = 20$
$\frac{1}{2}$ of $10 = 5$
25 people went to work on the bus

★ Thursday $10 \times 2 = 20$ people went to work on the bus

★ Friday $10 \times 3 = 30$ people went to work on the bus

★ Saturday $10 \times 1 = 10$
$\frac{1}{2}$ of $10 = 5$
15 people went to work on the bus

★ Sunday $\frac{1}{2}$ of $10 = 5$ people went to work on the bus

We can also see clearly the answers to these questions:

On which day did the most number of people travel on the bus? ***Friday***

On which day did the least number of people travel on the bus? ***Sunday***

When did 25 people travel on the bus? ***Wednesday***

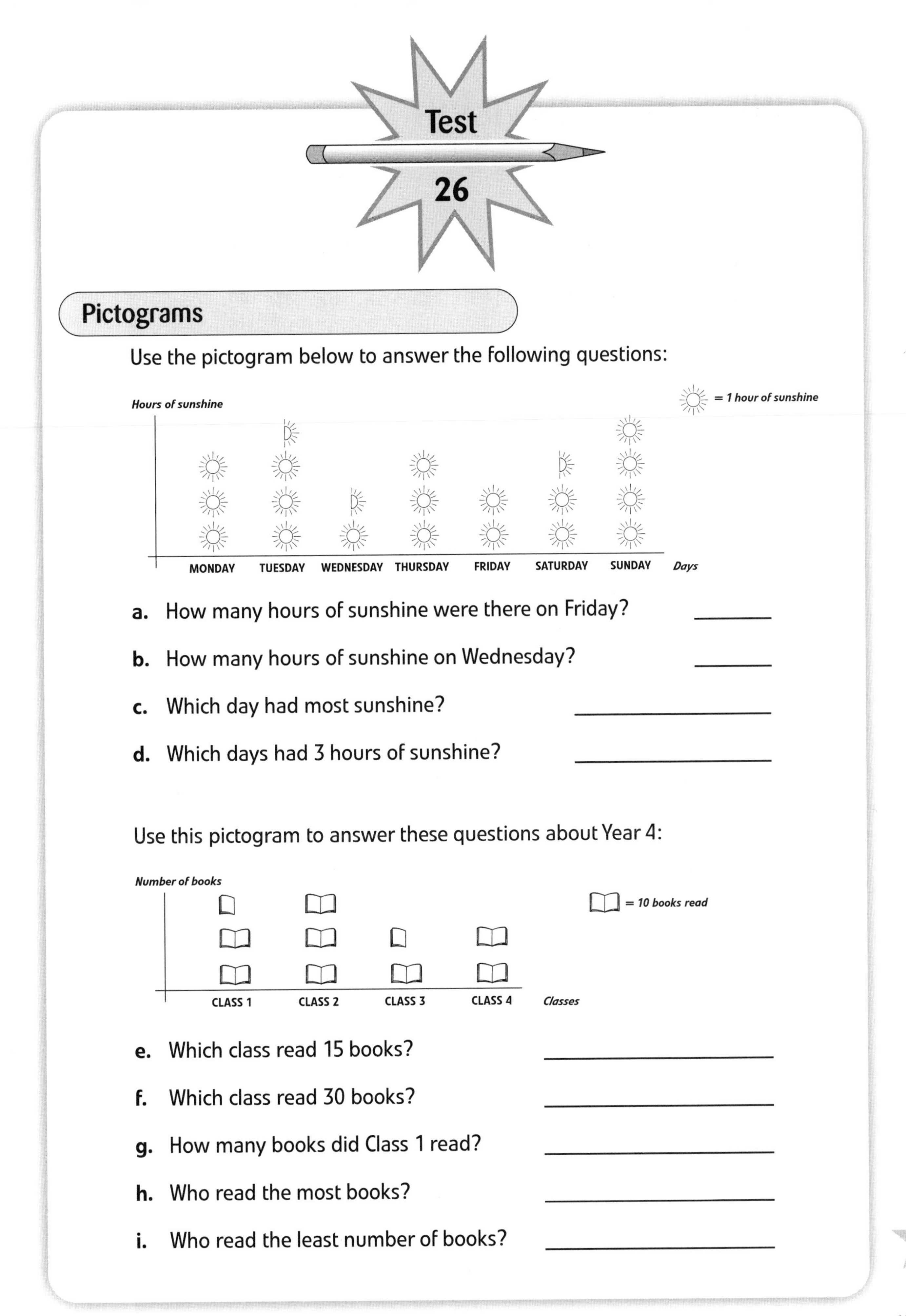

Test 26

Pictograms

Use the pictogram below to answer the following questions:

a. How many hours of sunshine were there on Friday? ______

b. How many hours of sunshine on Wednesday? ______

c. Which day had most sunshine? ______

d. Which days had 3 hours of sunshine? ______

Use this pictogram to answer these questions about Year 4:

e. Which class read 15 books? ______

f. Which class read 30 books? ______

g. How many books did Class 1 read? ______

h. Who read the most books? ______

i. Who read the least number of books? ______

Handling data: Revision

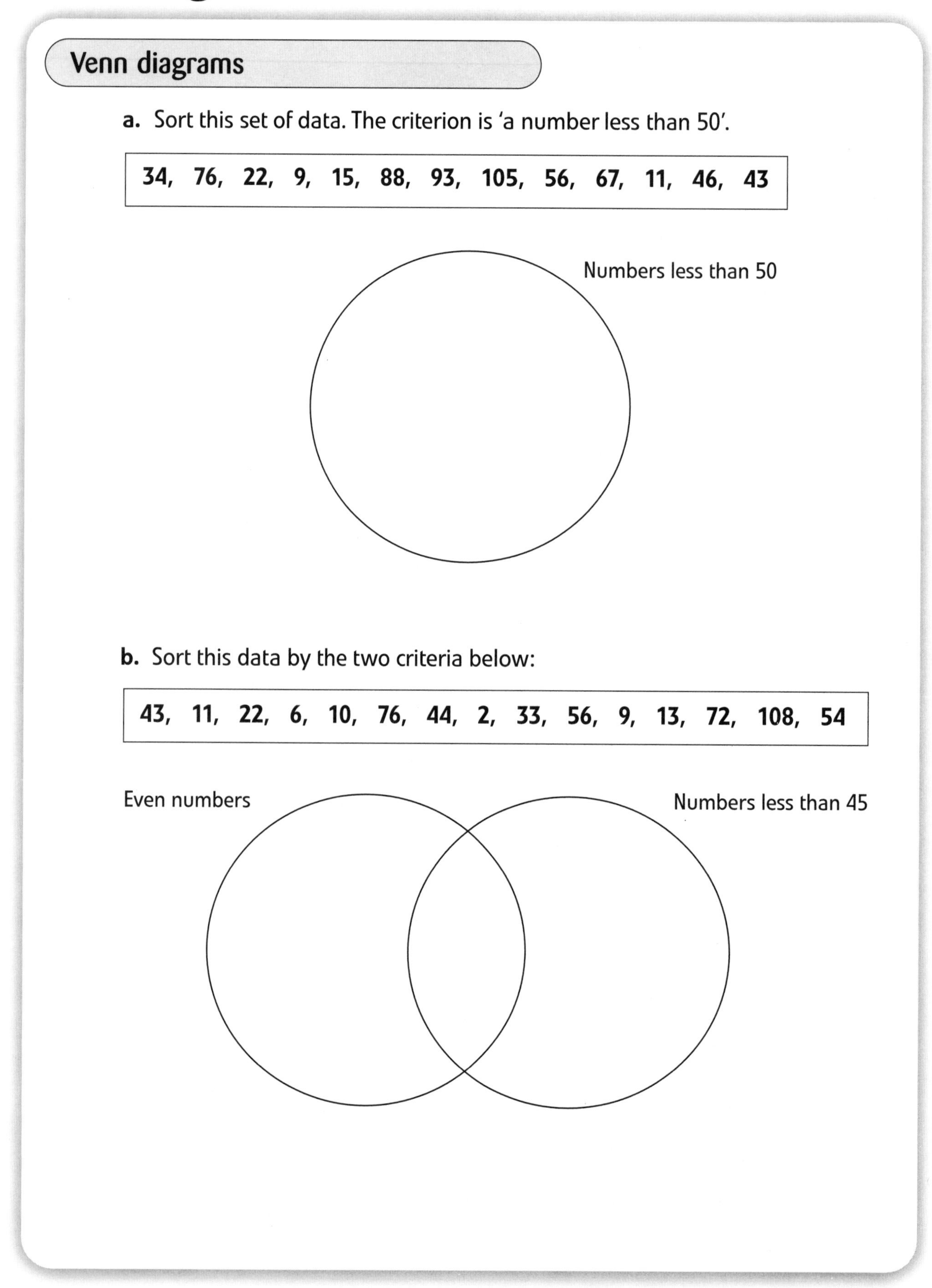

Venn diagrams

a. Sort this set of data. The criterion is 'a number less than 50'.

34, 76, 22, 9, 15, 88, 93, 105, 56, 67, 11, 46, 43

b. Sort this data by the two criteria below:

43, 11, 22, 6, 10, 76, 44, 2, 33, 56, 9, 13, 72, 108, 54

Venn diagrams 2

a. Use the headings 'hot' and 'drinks' to classify this data:

coffee, tea, chips, salad, apple, orange juice, cola, burger, milk

b. What could the headings be?

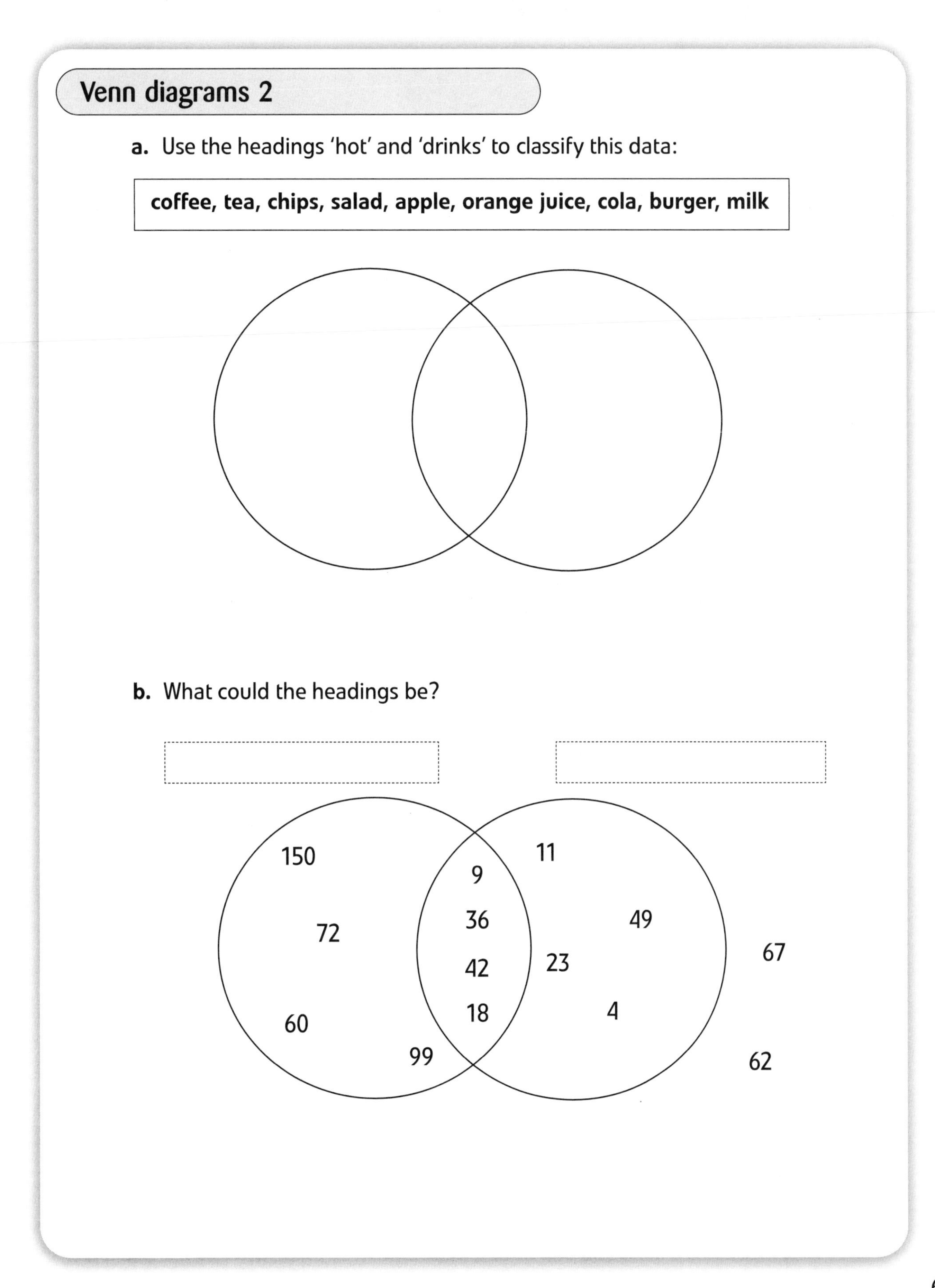

Handling data: Revision

Carroll diagrams 1

a. Sort this set of data:

35, 24, 11, 98, 105, 37, 45, 80, 25, 7, 52, 225, 192, 15

Multiples of 5	Not multiples of 5

b. Now sort the same data into this carroll diagram with extra criteria:

	Multiples of 5	Not multiples of 5
Even numbers		
Not even numbers		

Carroll diagrams 2

a. Sort this set of data:

netball, football, swimming, basketball, running, tennis, skiing, gymnastics, rugby, motor racing

A sport using a ball	A sport not using a ball

b. What could the headings be?

	Whales Dolphins Seals Walrus	Shark Octopus
	Monkeys Humans Tigers	Tortoise Blackbird Butterfly

Handling data: Revision

Bar charts

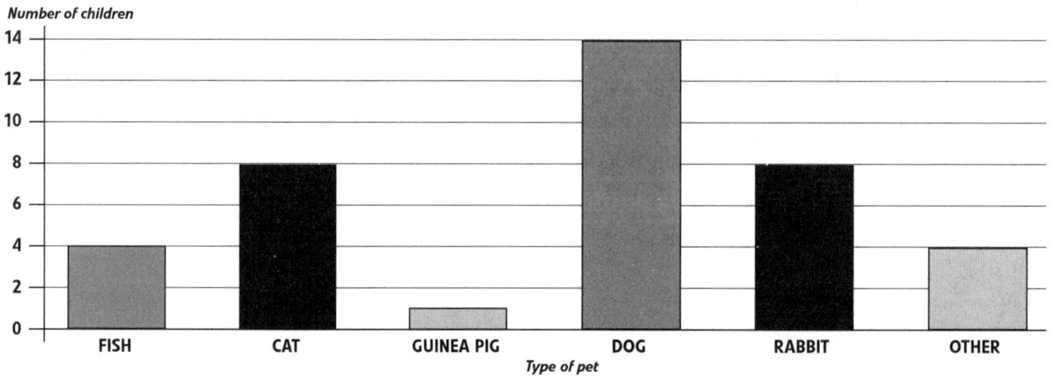

Number of children

14
12
10
8
6
4
2
0

FISH CAT GUINEA PIG DOG RABBIT OTHER

Type of pet

During a survey, a class of children were asked to name their favourite pet. Use this bar chart to answer the following questions:

a. How many children said that a dog was their favourite pet? ___________

b. What was the least favourite pet? ___________

c. How many children were in the survey? ___________

d. Which pets did eight children choose? ___________

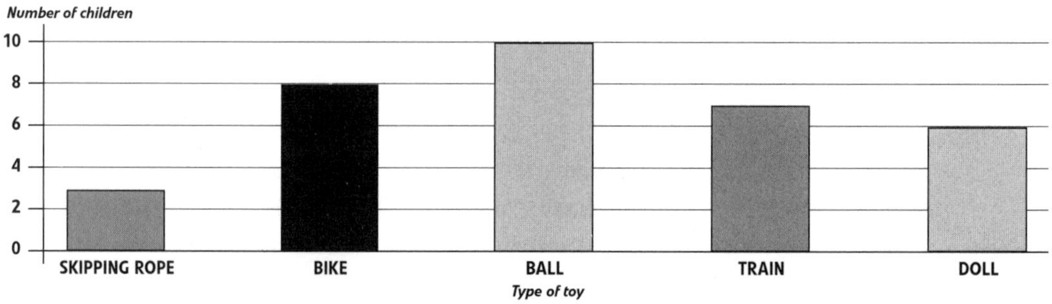

Number of children

10
8
6
4
2
0

SKIPPING ROPE BIKE BALL TRAIN DOLL

Type of toy

A group of children were asked about their favourite toy. Use this bar chart to answer the following questions:

e. How many children said bike? ___________

f. Which toy was the overall favourite? ___________

g. Four more children were asked the question – 2 said train, 1 said doll and 1 said skipping rope. What are the new totals for these three toys?

Train ___________ Doll ___________ Skipping rope ___________

Tally charts

a. Use the tally chart to record the number of letters in the sentence below:

Tally charts help us to record and collect lots of information quickly.

Type of letter	Tally	Total
Vowel		
Consonant		

b. Write down the names of 8 people in your class at school. Use the tally chart to find out how many vowels and consonants are in their names.

Type of letter	Tally	Total
Vowel		
Consonant		

Handling data: Revision

Drawing bar charts

a. Use the information in the frequency table below to complete the bar chart:

Favourite drinks	Number of children
Milk	3
Water	2
Cola	10
Orange squash	8
Blackcurrant	11
Lemonade	5

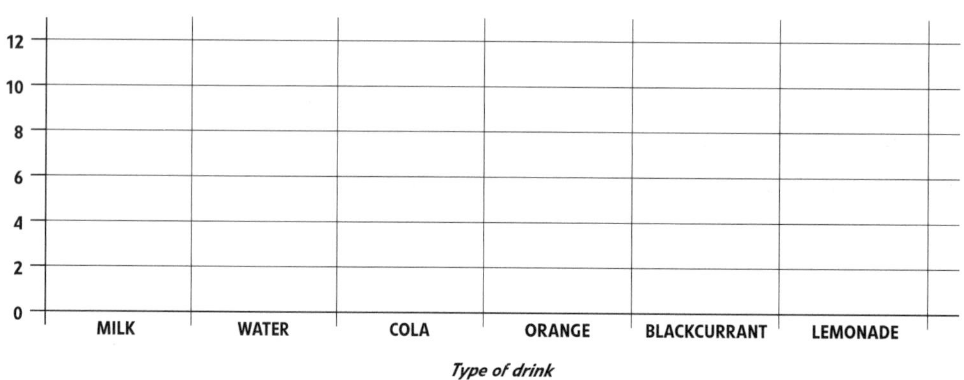

b. Complete this tally chart of a bird watch survey, and use it to fill in the bar chart below:

Type of bird	Tally	Total
Blackbird	𝍸 III	
Sparrow	𝍸 𝍸 𝍸 I	
Bluetit	𝍸 I	
Chaffinch	III	
Unknown	𝍸 IIII	

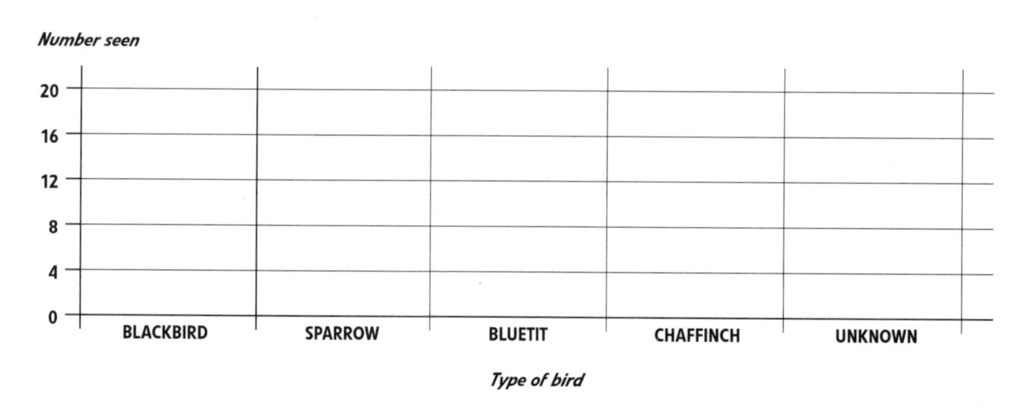

Frequency tables

Use the bar chart below to complete the frequency table:

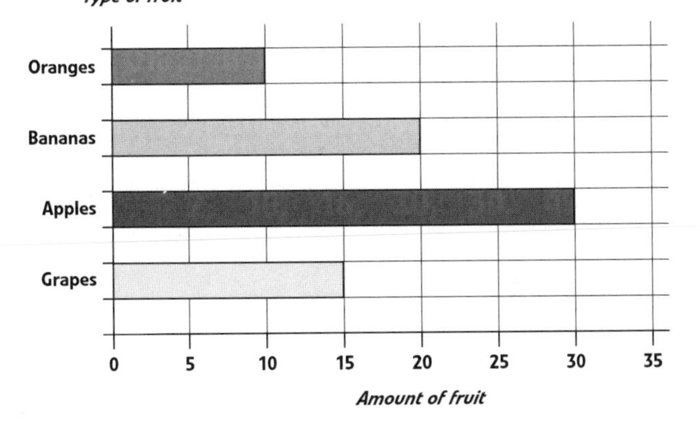

Type of fruit	Amount of fruit

Pictograms

Use the information in the pictogram below to answer the following questions:

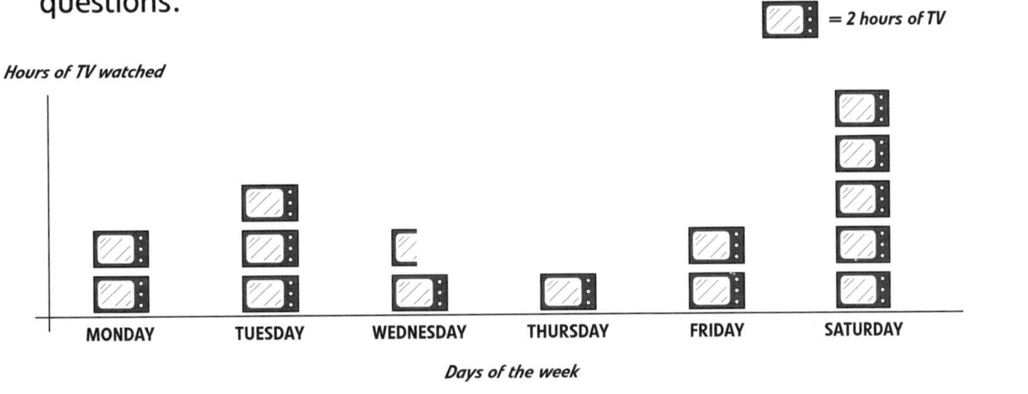

a. How many hours of television were watched on Wednesday? ________

b. How many **more** hours were watched on Tuesday? ________

c. On which day was the least amount of television watched? ________

d. How many hours of television were watched altogether? ________

e. Explain why you think more hours were watched on Saturday than any other day.

____

____

Polygons

2-dimensional shapes

A ***polygon*** is any ***two dimensional*** (2-D) shape made up of ***three or more straight sides.***

We are going to look at some polygons and their properties:

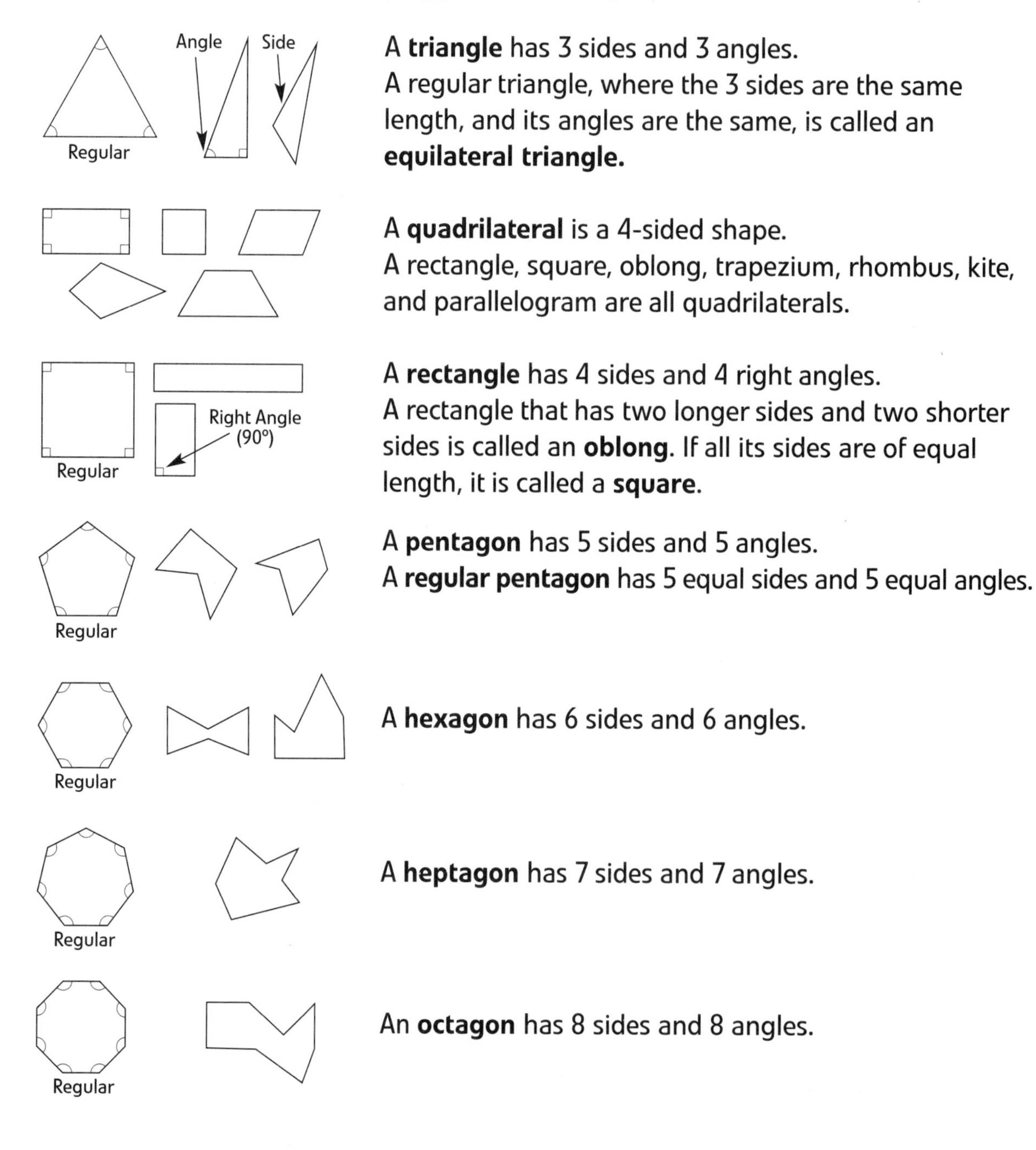

A **triangle** has 3 sides and 3 angles.
A regular triangle, where the 3 sides are the same length, and its angles are the same, is called an **equilateral triangle.**

A **quadrilateral** is a 4-sided shape.
A rectangle, square, oblong, trapezium, rhombus, kite, and parallelogram are all quadrilaterals.

A **rectangle** has 4 sides and 4 right angles.
A rectangle that has two longer sides and two shorter sides is called an **oblong**. If all its sides are of equal length, it is called a **square**.

A **pentagon** has 5 sides and 5 angles.
A **regular pentagon** has 5 equal sides and 5 equal angles.

A **hexagon** has 6 sides and 6 angles.

A **heptagon** has 7 sides and 7 angles.

An **octagon** has 8 sides and 8 angles.

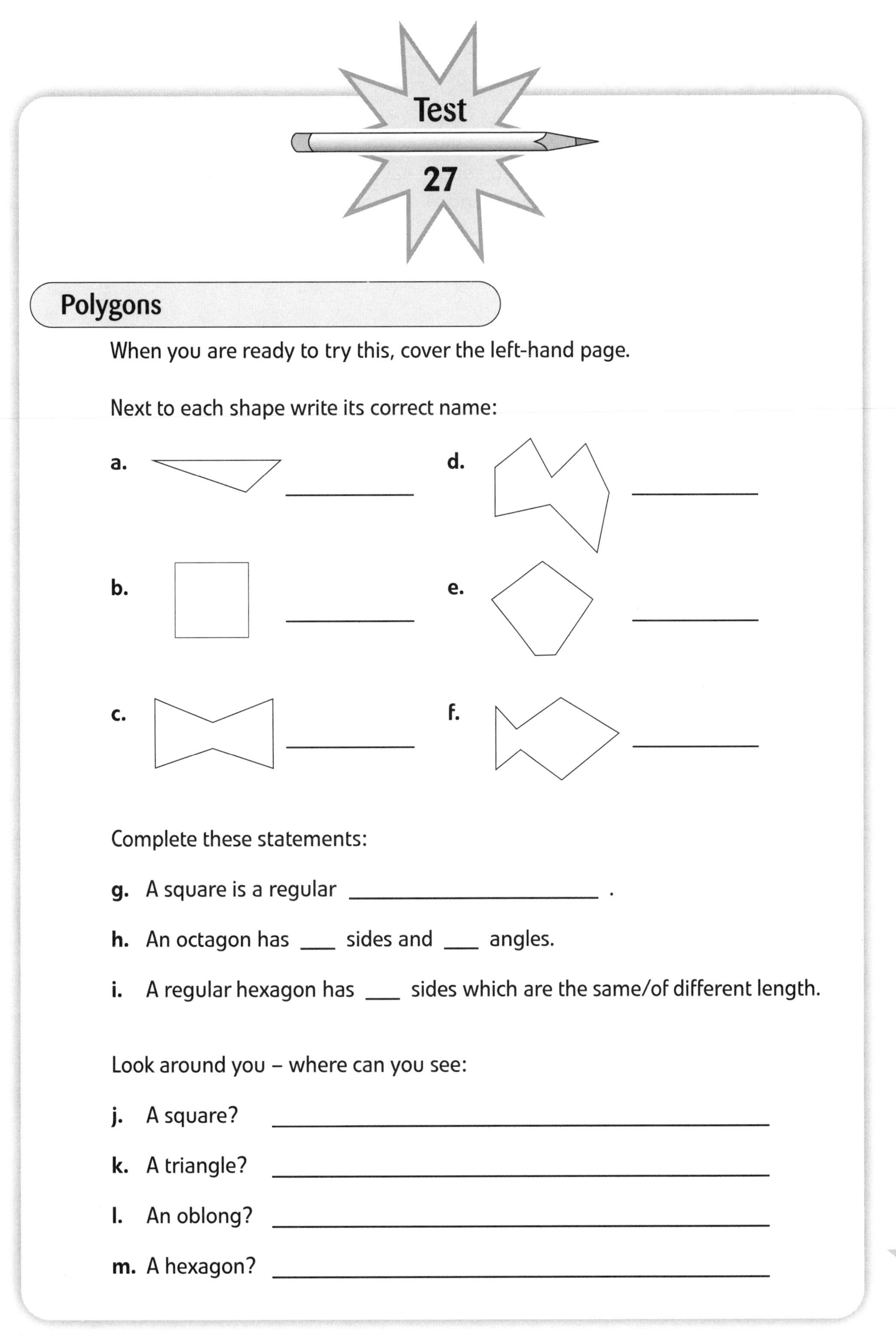

Test 27

Polygons

When you are ready to try this, cover the left-hand page.

Next to each shape write its correct name:

a. ____________

b. ____________

c. ____________

d. ____________

e. ____________

f. ____________

Complete these statements:

g. A square is a regular ____________________ .

h. An octagon has ___ sides and ___ angles.

i. A regular hexagon has ___ sides which are the same/of different length.

Look around you – where can you see:

j. A square? ________________________________

k. A triangle? ________________________________

l. An oblong? ________________________________

m. A hexagon? ________________________________

3-D shapes

3-D means ***three dimensional***. 3-D shapes have ***length***, ***width*** and ***height***. They are sometimes called solids. They are found all around us.

We will now look at some 3-D shapes and their properties:

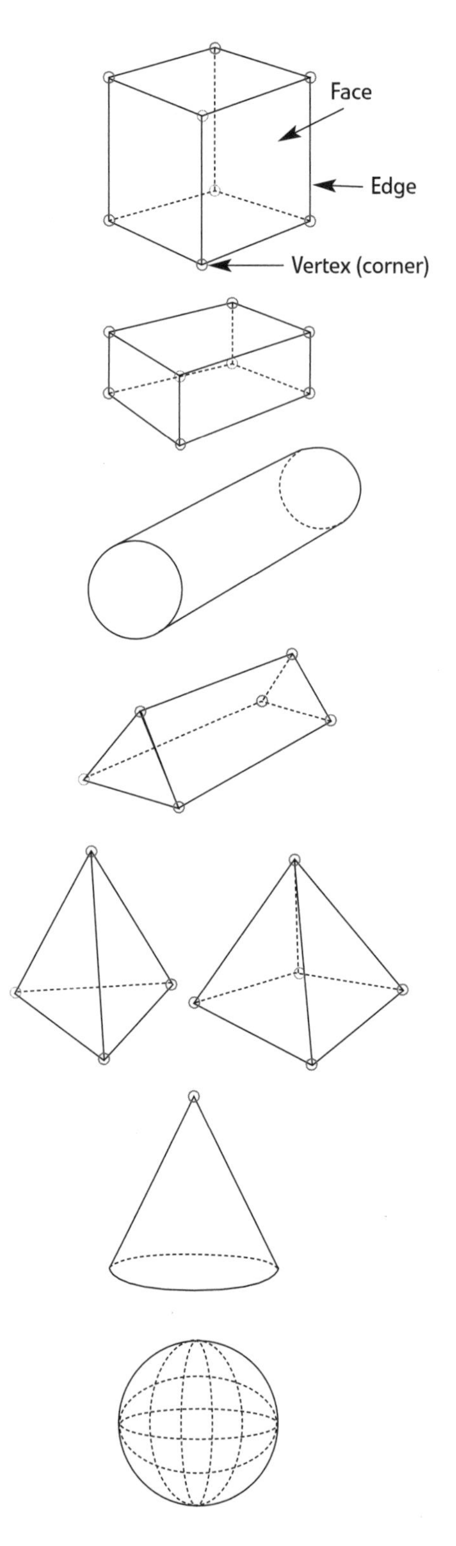

A **cube** has 6 faces, 8 vertices and 12 edges. Each face is a square.

A **cuboid** has the same properties as a cube, except that its faces are all rectangles. Opposite faces are the same size.

A **cylinder** has 2 flat faces (circles) and one curved face. If we flattened it out it would be a rectangle. It is sometimes called a **circular prism** because any slice of it (the cross section) is always a circle.

A **triangular prism** has 5 faces, 6 vertices and 9 edges. It has the cross section of a triangle.

A **tetrahedron** is a **triangular-based pyramid.**
It has 4 triangular faces, 4 vertices and 6 edges.
You may also see **square-based pyramids** or even **hexagonal-based pyramids.**

A **cone** is similar to a pyramid. It has one flat face (circle) and one curved face. It has one vertex.

A **sphere** is a circular solid, where any point on its surface is always the same distance from its centre.

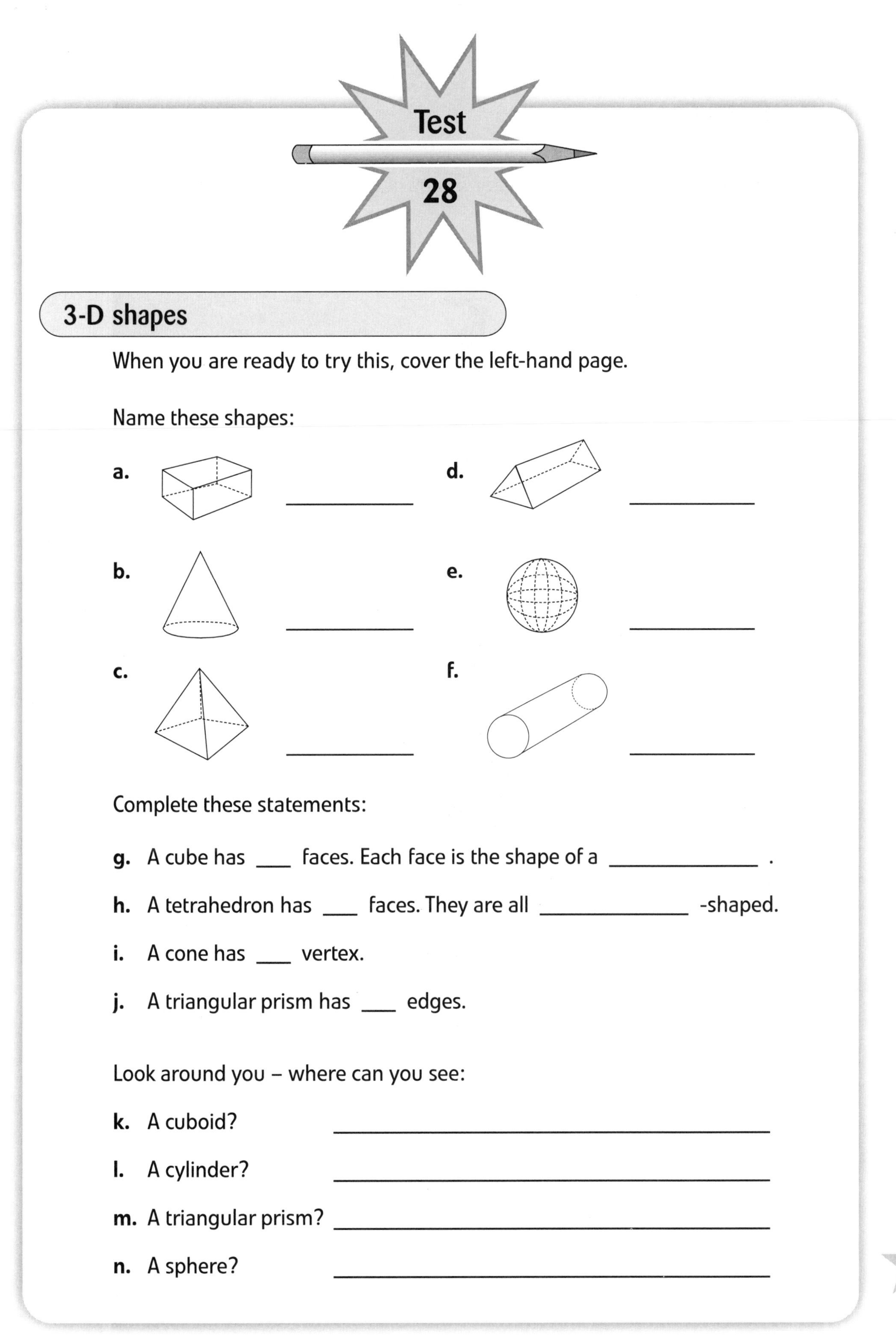

Test 28

3-D shapes

When you are ready to try this, cover the left-hand page.

Name these shapes:

a. ____________ **d.** ____________

b. ____________ **e.** ____________

c. ____________ **f.** ____________

Complete these statements:

g. A cube has ___ faces. Each face is the shape of a ____________ .

h. A tetrahedron has ___ faces. They are all ____________ -shaped.

i. A cone has ___ vertex.

j. A triangular prism has ___ edges.

Look around you – where can you see:

k. A cuboid? ______________________________

l. A cylinder? ______________________________

m. A triangular prism? ______________________________

n. A sphere? ______________________________

Symmetry

Symmetry is like looking at a ***mirror image*** of a shape, or part of a shape.

We can make shapes symmetrical by sketching in the reflection of the shape using a mirror line.

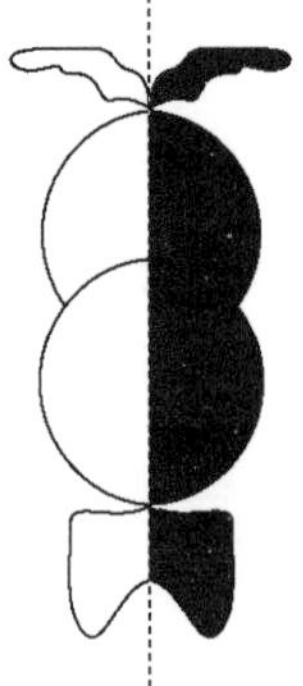

Here, you can see that the shaded area is a reflection of the original shape.

We can also look for lines of symmetry in complete shapes – this is when we can see a line along which it would be possible to fold the shape into two exact halves, both being the same shape.

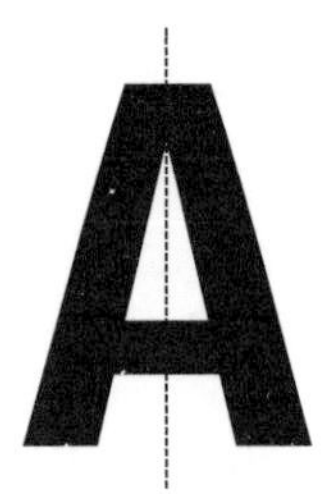

This letter A has one line of symmetry – shown by the dotted line. If we folded along the dotted line, the two pieces would fit exactly on top of each other.

Regular polygons – squares, triangles and circles – also have lines of symmetry. Sometimes there is more than one line of symmetry.

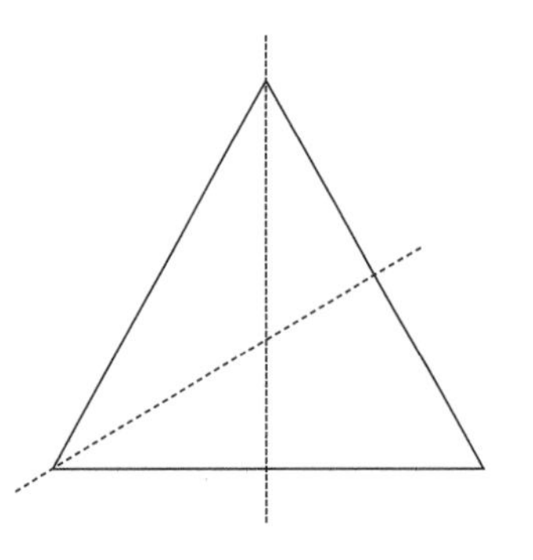

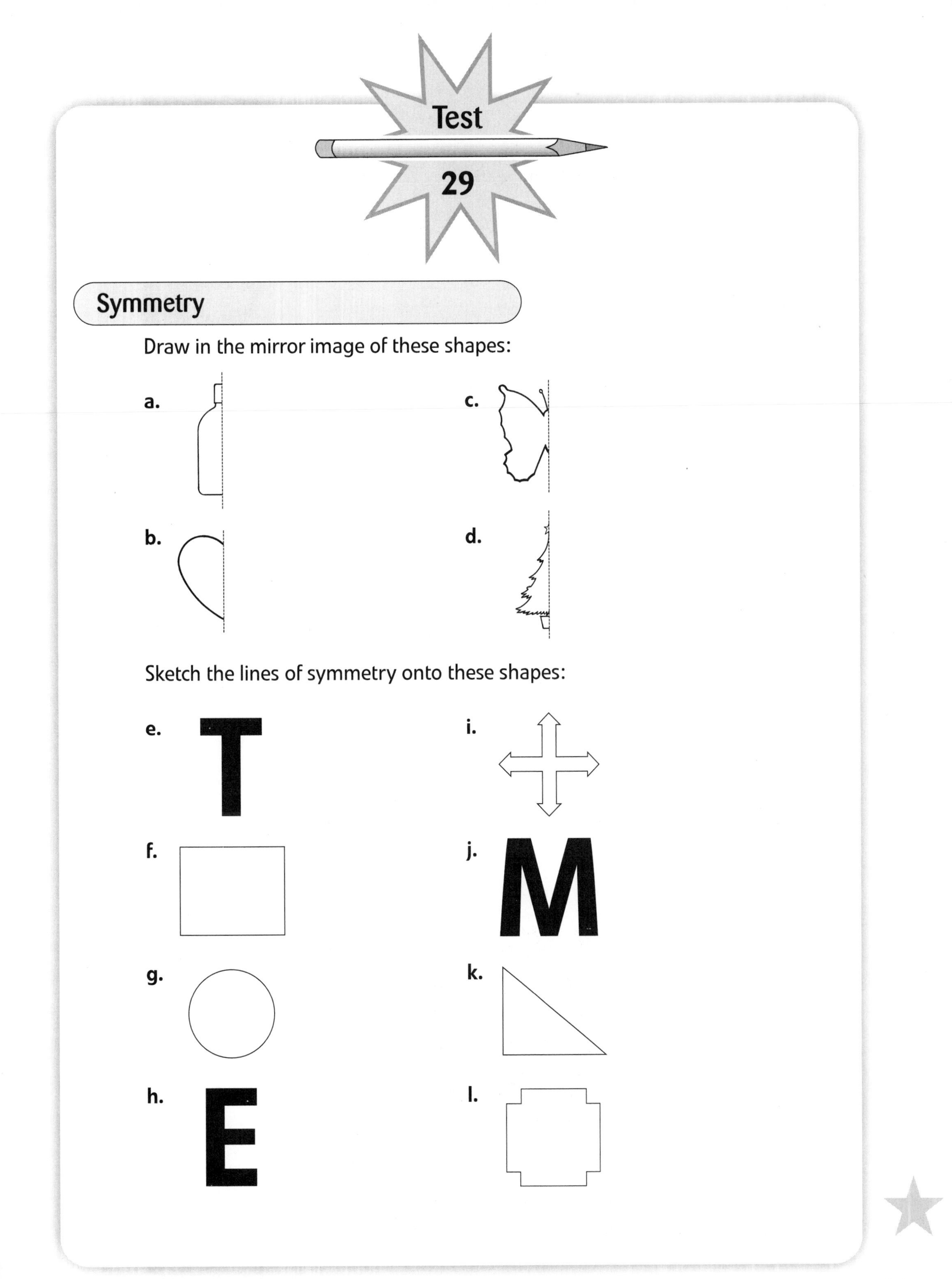

Test 29

Symmetry

Draw in the mirror image of these shapes:

a.

b.

c.

d.

Sketch the lines of symmetry onto these shapes:

e.

f.

g.

h.

i.

j.

k.

l.

Area

The ***area*** is the ***space covered by a shape***.

If a shape is drawn on a centimetre-square grid, we can count the number of squares that the shape covers. This will then give us the area, in cm^2.

For example:

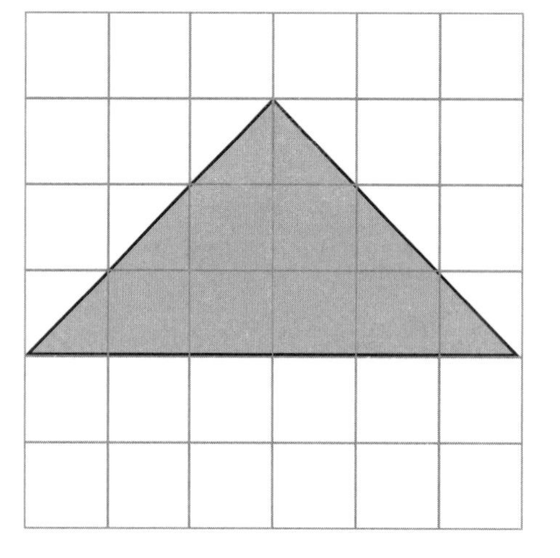

If we count the number of squares covered by this shape, we can see that there are:

6 whole squares
6 halves of squares, which make 3 whole squares

This means that the area is a total of $9cm^2$.

When calculating areas of simple rectangles, we can move on from counting the number of squares, to using the length and width of the shape.

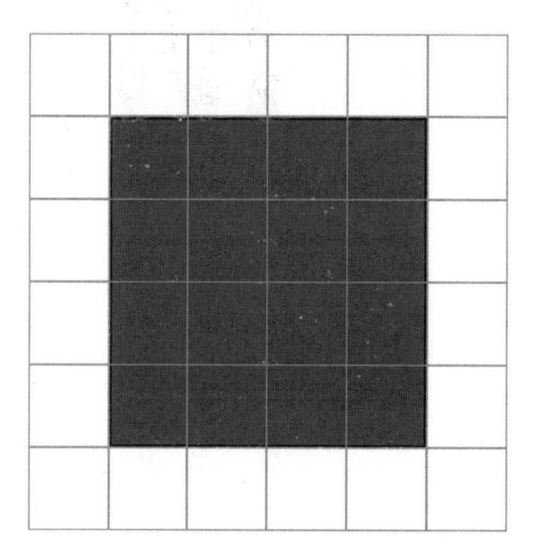

The area of this rectangle is $16cm^2$ (4 rows of 4).
We can simplify this to $4 \times 4 = 16$ (length x width).

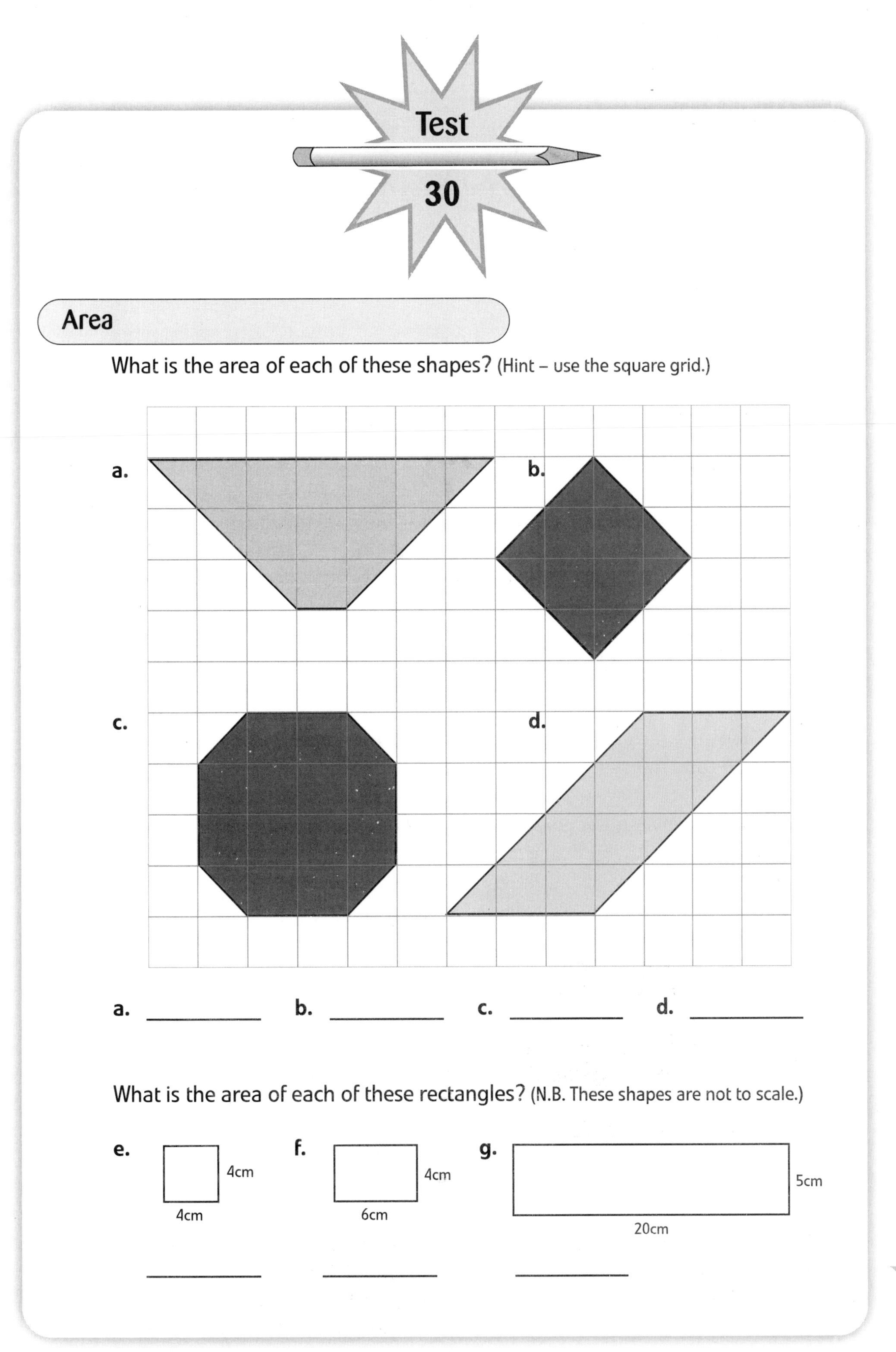

Test 30

Area

What is the area of each of these shapes? (Hint – use the square grid.)

a.
b.
c.
d.

a. ____________ b. ____________ c. ____________ d. ____________

What is the area of each of these rectangles? (N.B. These shapes are not to scale.)

e. 4cm 4cm
f. 4cm 6cm
g. 5cm 20cm

____________ ____________ ____________

Perimeter

The ***perimeter*** is the ***distance around the outside edge of any shape.***

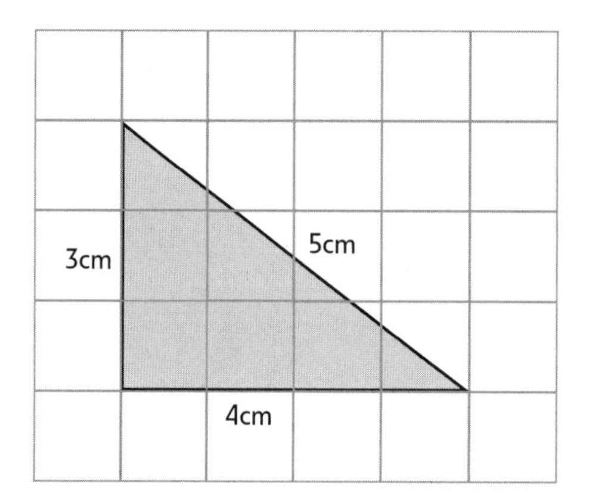

In calculating the perimeter of this shape, we measure the distance around the edge – 3cm, 4cm and 5cm:

3cm + 4cm + 5cm = 12cm

It is simple to calculate the perimeter of any shape if we know its dimensions. We can add them all up – as shown above.

If the shape is a rectangle, the opposite sides are of equal length, so we can double the lengths and the widths.

If the shape is any regular polygon, we just multiply the length of the side by the number of sides.

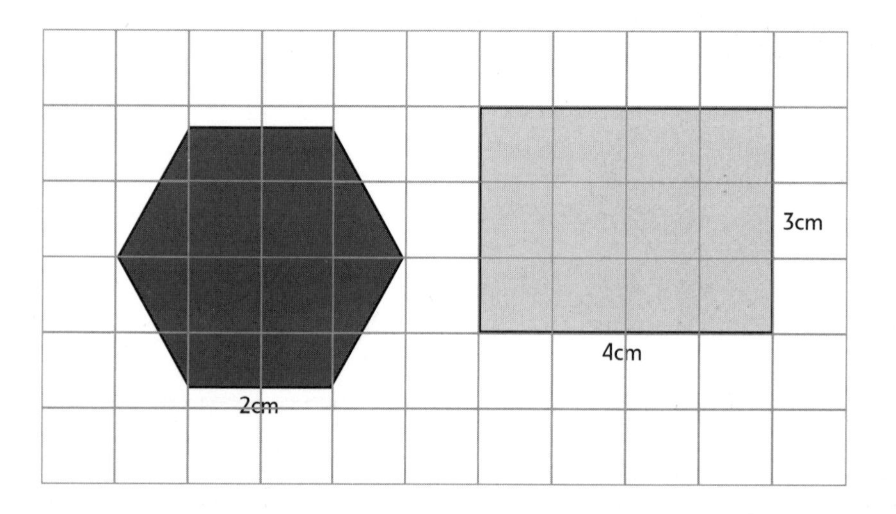

The hexagon has sides of 2cm:
therefore the perimeter is
6 x 2 = 12cm

The rectangle has two sides of 3cm
and two of 4cm:
therefore the perimeter is
3 x 2 (= 6) + 4 x 2 (= 8) = 14cm

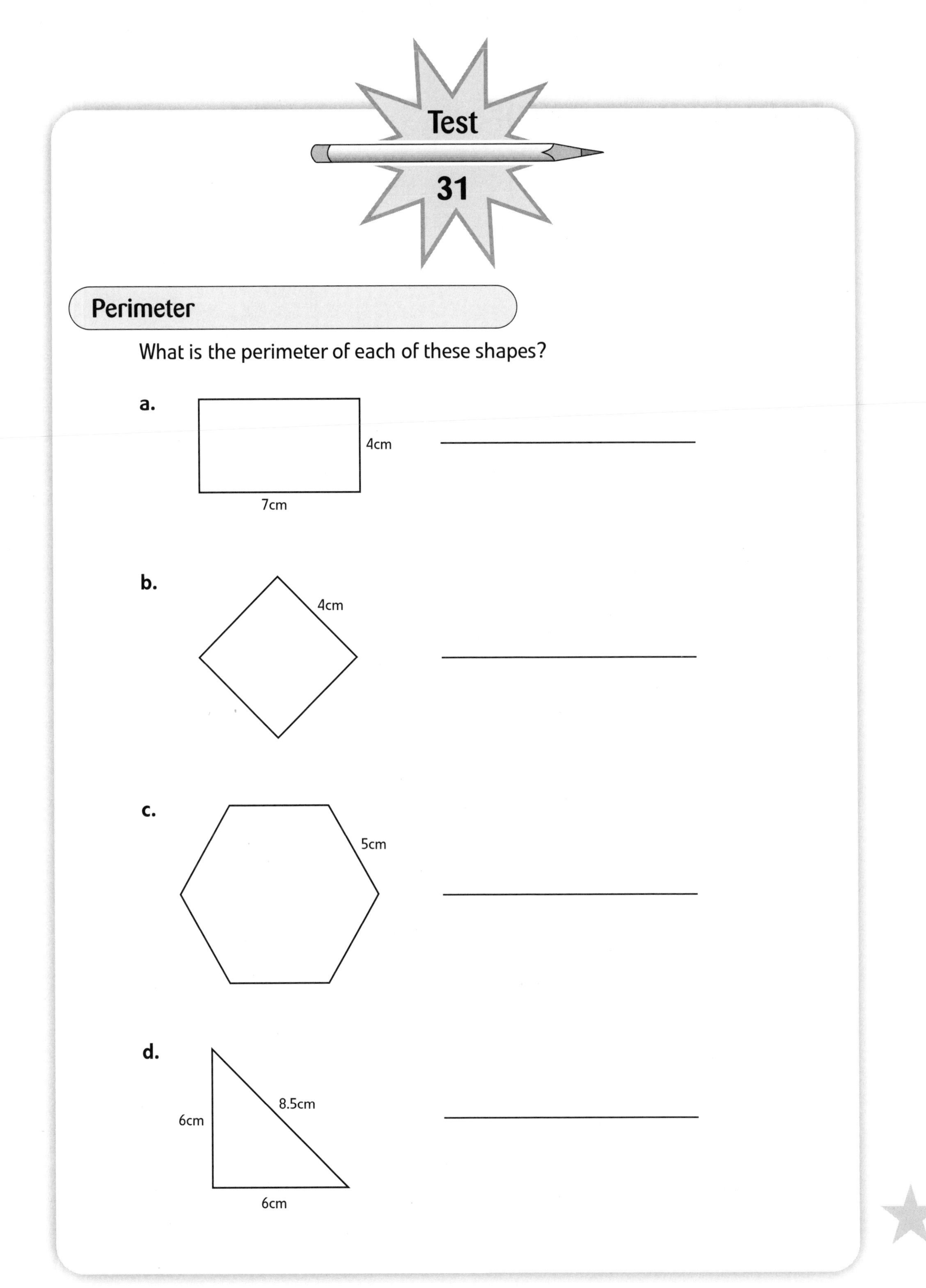

Perimeter

What is the perimeter of each of these shapes?

a.

b.

c.

d.

Geometry: Revision

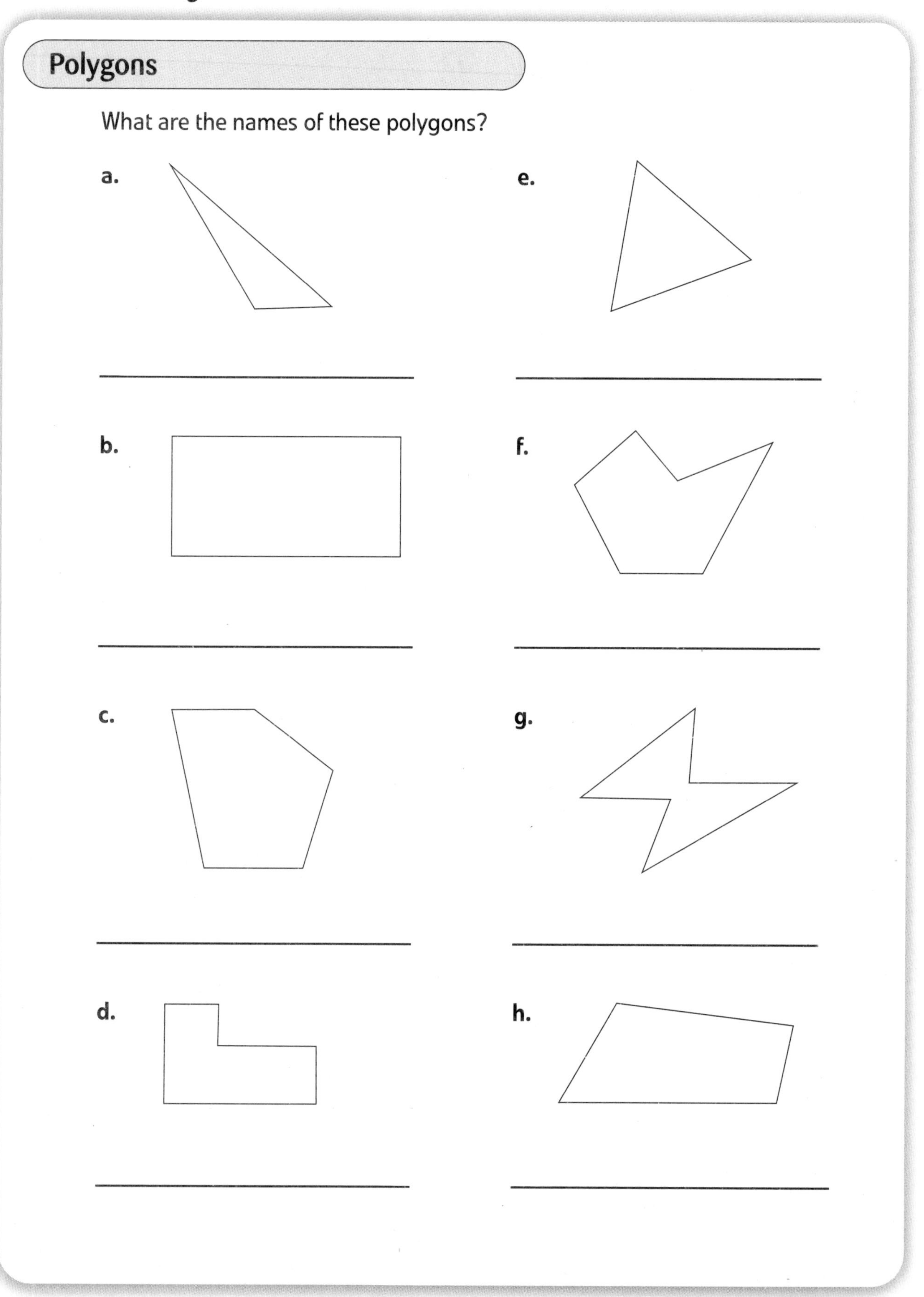

Polygons

What are the names of these polygons?

Properties of shapes

a. How many sides does a triangle have? ____________

b. How many sides does a heptagon have? ____________

c. A polygon with 8 sides is called an ____________

d. A polygon must have three or more straight sides – true or false? ____________

e. I have four sides. They are all equal in length. I have four right angles.

What am I? ____________

f. I have 6 sides. They are all different lengths.

What am I? ____________

g. I have 3 sides and 3 angles. They are all equal.

What am I? ____________

h. I have 4 sides and 4 angles. 2 of my sides are the same (shorter) length, and 2 of my sides are the same (longer) length. The angles are all right angles.

What am I? ____________

Geometry: Revision

Drawing shapes

a. Complete this shape to make a square:

b. Draw two different triangles:

c. Complete this shape to make a hexagon:

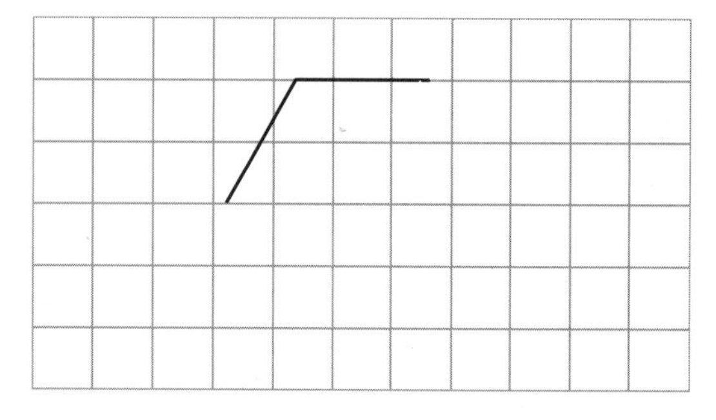

d. Draw three other shapes and write their names underneath:

3-D Shapes

a. What are the three dimensions that make up a 3-D shape?

______________ ______________ ______________

b. How many faces does a cube have? ______________

c. What 2-D shape are a cube's faces? ______________

d. How many edges does a sphere have? ______________

e. A triangular prism has 5 faces – what two 2-D shapes are they?

______________ and ______________

f. What 3-D shape is a tissue box? ______________

g. What shape is a ball? ______________

h. Complete the table below:

3-D Shape	Number of faces	Number of vertices	Number of edges
Cube	6	8	12
Cuboid			
Cone			
Triangular prism			
Tetrahedron			
Cylinder			

i. Go on a shape hunt around your house and outside. Use this tally chart to record your findings.

3-D Shape	Tally	Total
Sphere		
Cuboid		
Cube		
Triangular Prism		

Geometry: Revision

Symmetry

Draw in the mirror image of these shapes:

a.

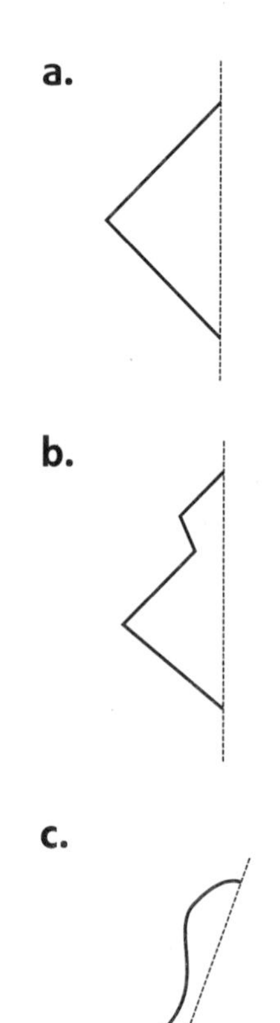

d.

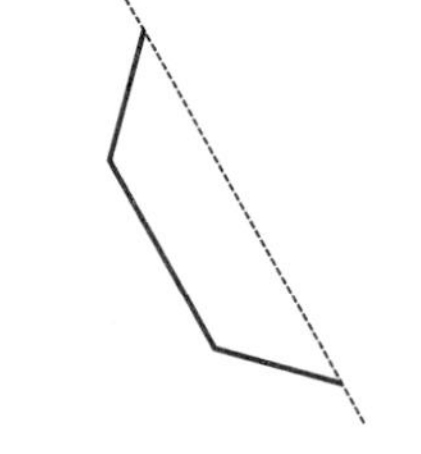

b.

e.

c.

f.

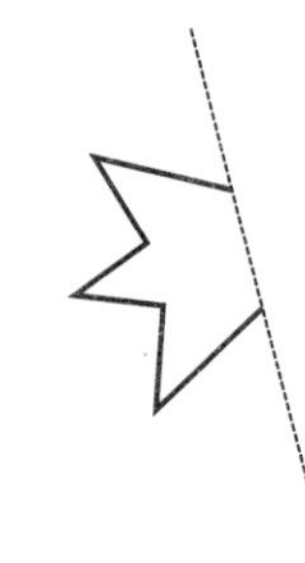

How many lines of symmetry are in:

g. A rectangle? __________

h. An equilateral triangle? __________

i. A regular hexagon? __________

j. The capital letter 'A'? __________

k. The capital letter 'B'? __________

l. The number '6'? __________

Area

What are the areas of these polygons:

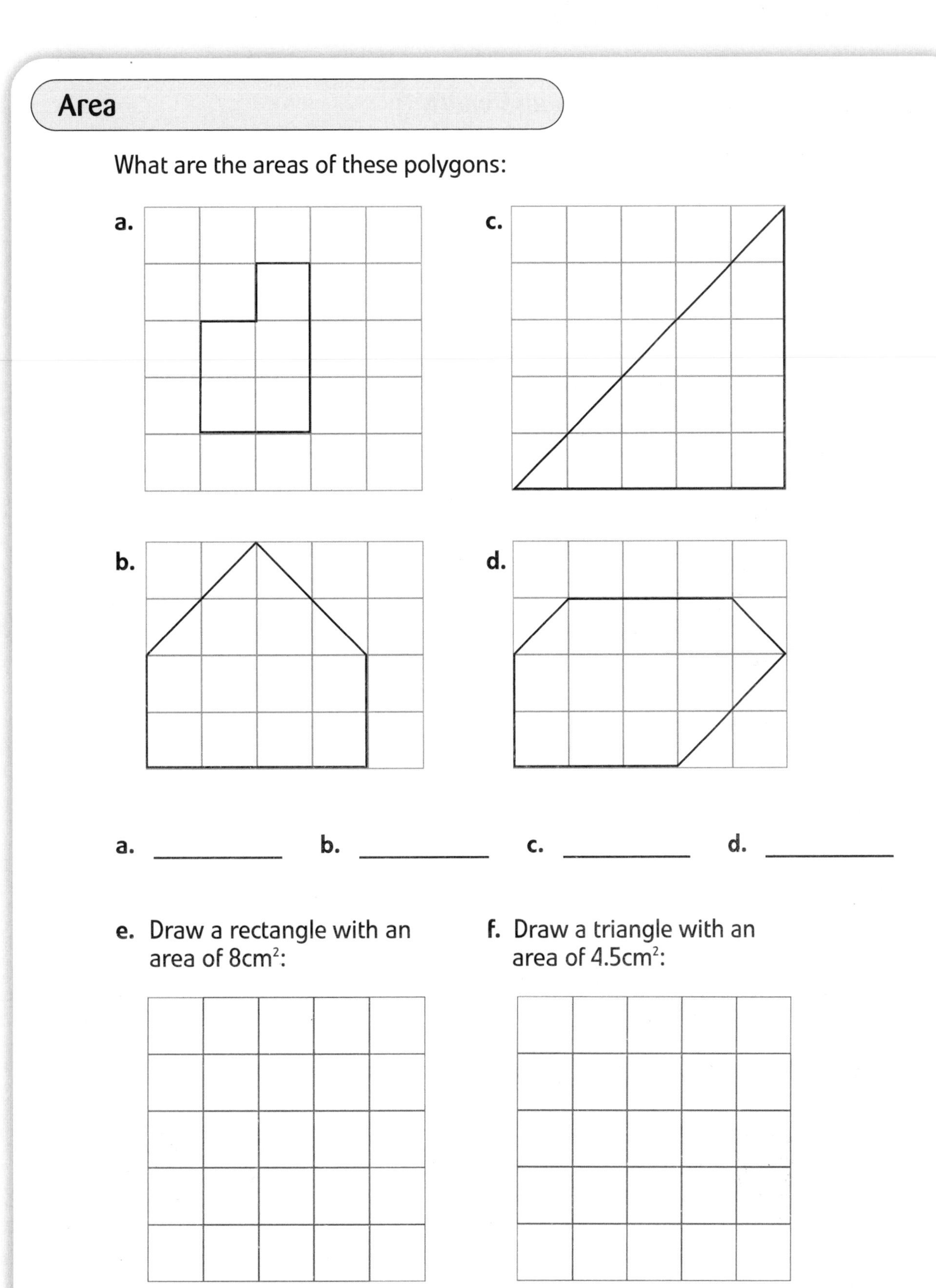

a. __________ b. __________ c. __________ d. __________

e. Draw a rectangle with an area of $8cm^2$:

f. Draw a triangle with an area of $4.5cm^2$:

Geometry: Revision

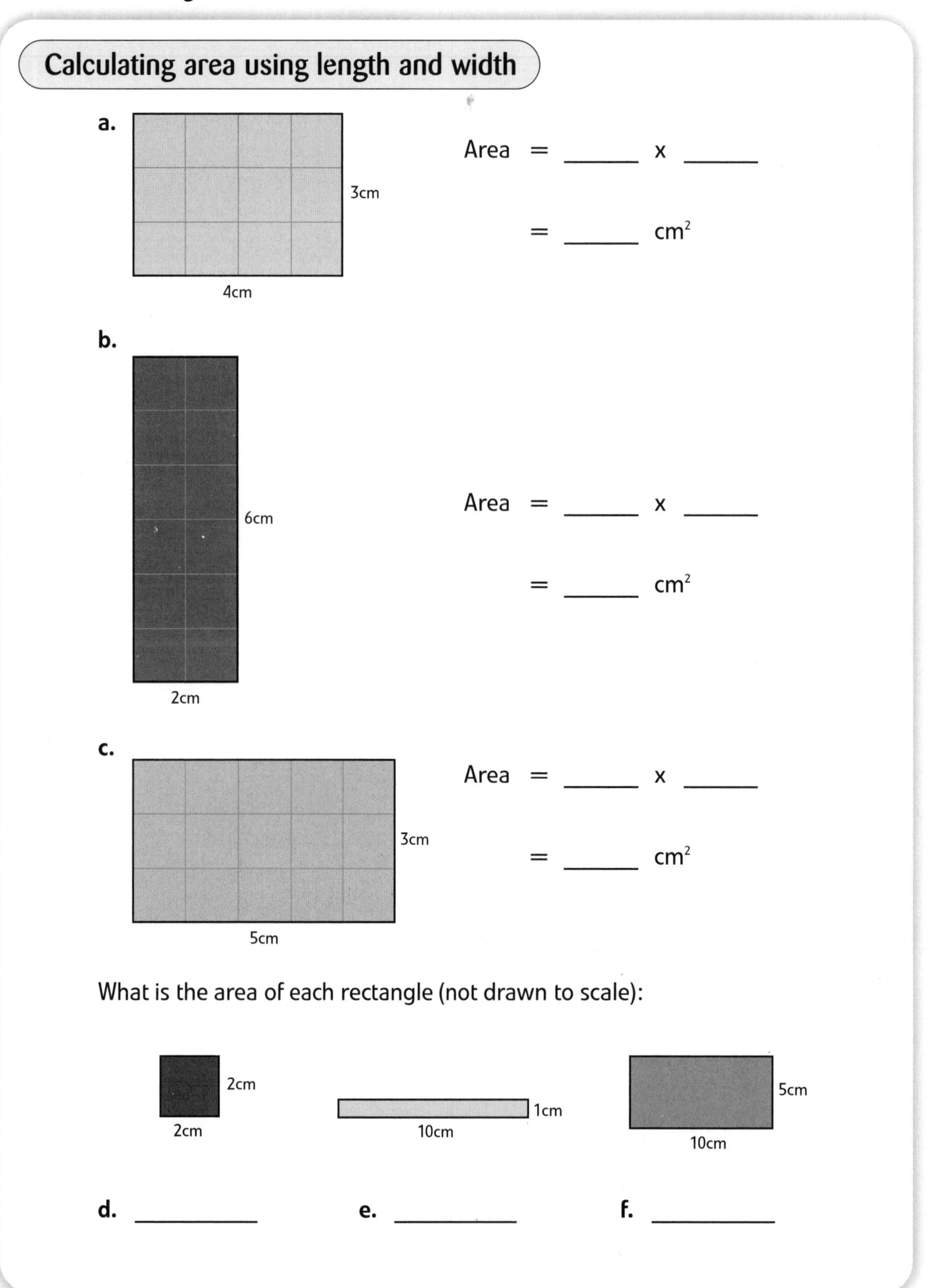

Calculating area using length and width

a.

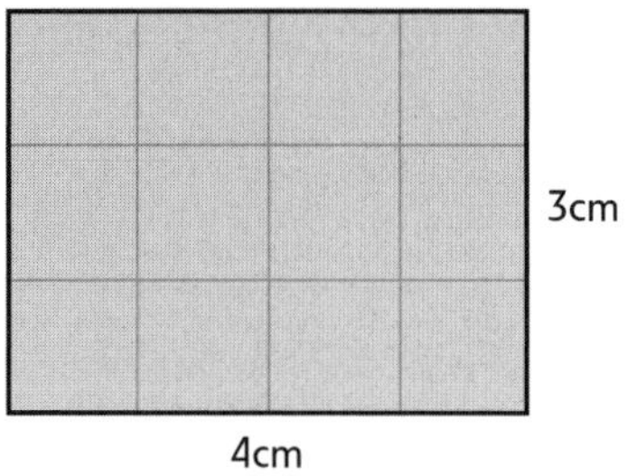

Area = ______ x ______

= ______ cm^2

b.

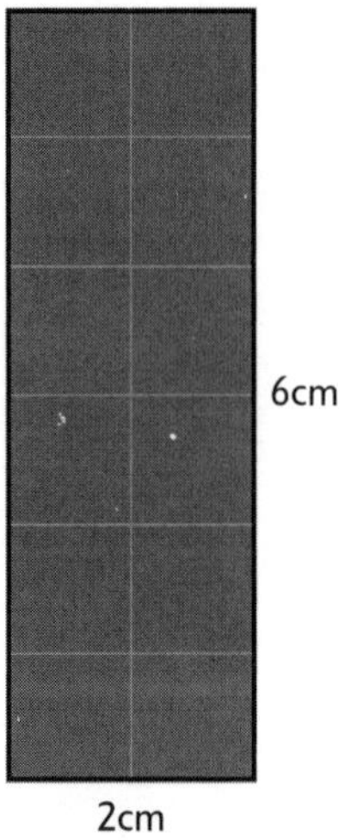

Area = ______ x ______

= ______ cm^2

c.

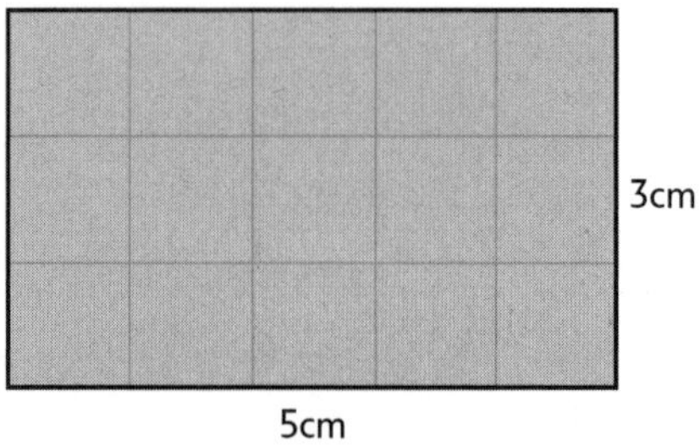

Area = ______ x ______

= ______ cm^2

What is the area of each rectangle (not drawn to scale):

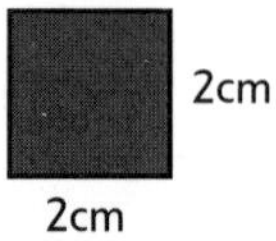

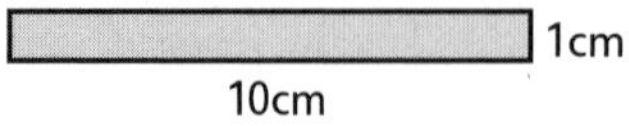

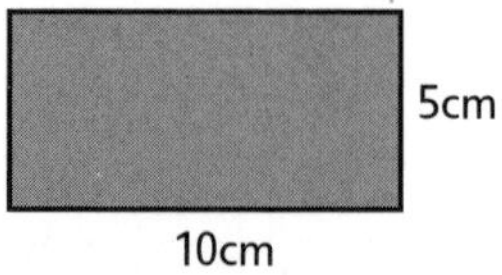

d. __________ **e.** __________ **f.** __________

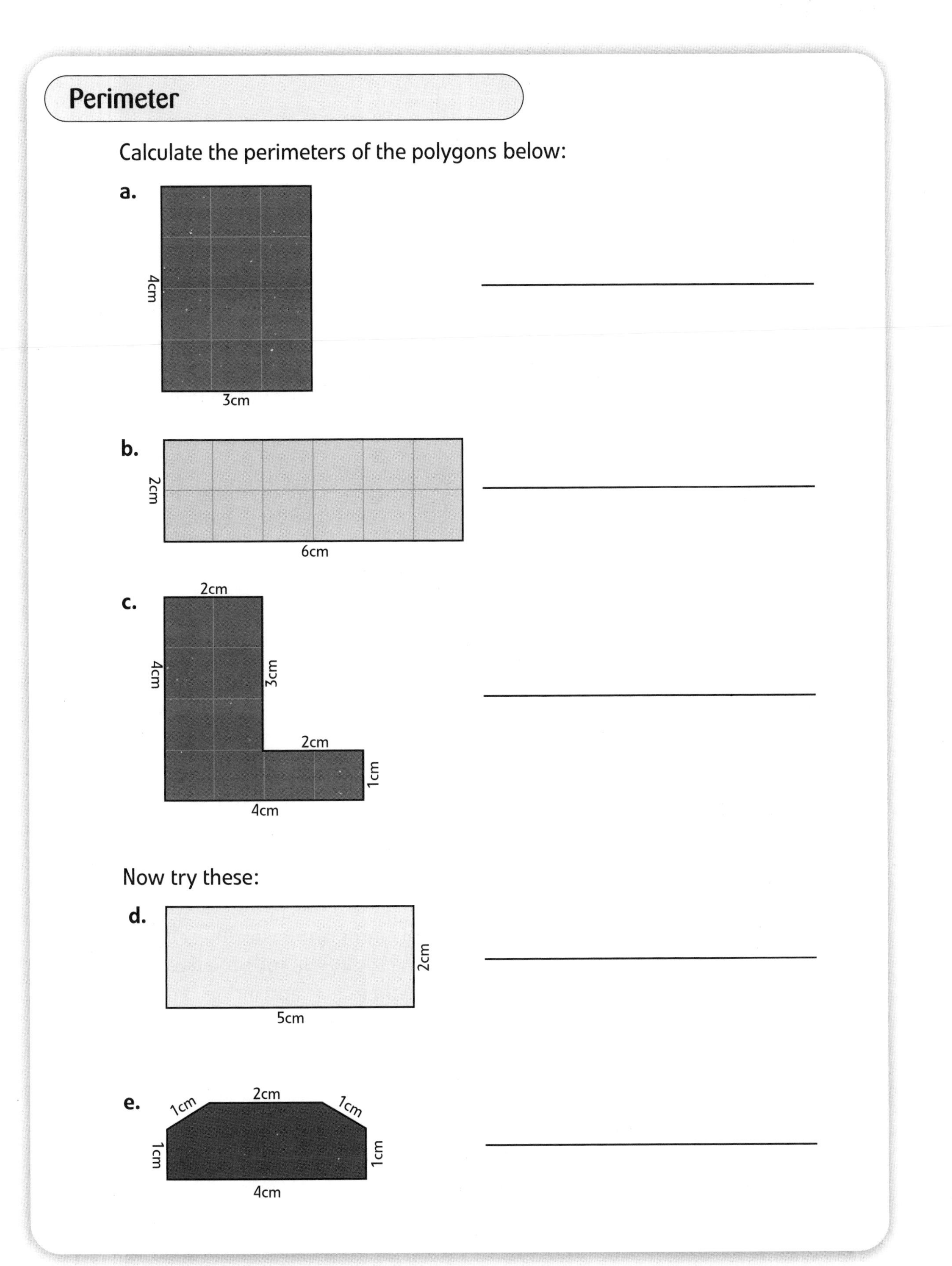

Perimeter

Calculate the perimeters of the polygons below:

a.

b.

c.

Now try these:

d.

e.

Length

Units of length

10 millimetres (mm) = 1 centimetre (cm)
100 centimetres (cm) = 1 metre (m)
1000 metres (m) = 1 kilometre (km)

Measuring equipment

We can measure length and distance using a variety of equipment. This includes rulers, tape measures, metre sticks and trundle wheels. Which one is appropriate will depend on what you are trying to measure. It would be difficult to measure the distance around your wrist using a ruler! And you would need a lot of metre sticks to measure the distance from your house to your school!

Using a ruler

When you look at a ruler, you will see that a millimetre is very small. It is easier to measure in centimetres.

When you measure a line, you need to make sure that the zero ('0') on your ruler is lined up with the end of the line.

0 1 2 3 4

You then need to look at the point where the line ends and read from the ruler the correct length (remembering that there are 10mm in a cm).

To draw a line, again you need to start at the zero and, holding the ruler steady, draw a line against the edge of the ruler until you reach the length you need.

Imperial measures

You may hear people talking about inches, feet, yards and miles. These are the old ***imperial measures*** that were replaced in the 1970s by the ***metric measures*** listed above. Many people may still describe their height in feet and inches, and road signs in the UK still show how many miles to a place, rather than how many kilometres.

To give you an idea of how big these measurements are:

1 inch = approximately 2.5cm
1 foot = 12 inches = approximately 30cm
1 yard = 3 feet = approximately 90cm
1 mile = 1760 yards = 5280 feet = approximately 1.6 kilometres

Test 32

Units of length

Which unit of length – millimetres, centimetres, metres, or kilometres – would you use to measure:

a. The length of your finger? ________________

b. The height of a house? ________________

c. The thickness of a plate? ________________

d. The length of a football pitch? ________________

e. The distance to Paris from your house? ________________

Measuring equipment

What would you use – a ruler, a tape measure, a metre stick, or a trundle wheel – to measure:

f. Around your head? ________________

g. The length of your school playground? ________________

h. The length of your pencil? ________________

Using a ruler

Find a ruler and measure these lines, writing your answers in the boxes provided:

i. ____________ [ ] cm

j. ____________________ [ ] cm

k. ____ [ ] cm

Capacity and mass

Units of capacity

Liquids are measured in units of ***capacity***. If you look on the side of a can of coke, or a bottle of squash you will see that they can be measured in ***litres***, ***centilitres*** or ***millilitres***.

10 millilitres (ml) = 1 centilitre (cl)
100 centilitres (cl) = 1 litre (l)
1000 millilitres (ml) = 1 litre (l)

Units of mass

Mass is measured in ***tonnes***, ***kilograms***, ***grams*** and ***milligrams***.

1000 milligrams (mg) = 1 gram (g)
1000 grams (g) = 1 kilogram (kg)
1000 kilograms (kg) = 1 tonne (t)

Reading scales

Mass is measured using weighing scales – you may have a set of scales in your kitchen which is used by your family when cooking. Capacity is usually measured using a jug or cylinder. All measuring equipment will have a scale, which you need to be able to read.

A scale is marked with ***divisions***. You need to work out what each of these represents.

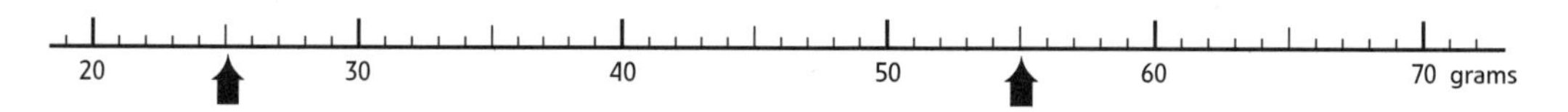

On this scale the main divisions go up in tens. The halfway point is also marked, but does not show a value. Half way between 20 and 30 is 25, half way between 50 and 60 is 55 etc. Therefore the arrows are pointing to 25 grams and 55 grams.

You can work out the value of unnumbered divisions by using your number skills. Look at how many divisions there are between the two main values and divide their difference by this number. So if a scale shows 20 to 30, and there are 10 divisions in between, each division is worth 1 (10 ÷ 10).

Weighing scales often have a circular scale but this can be read in exactly the same way, and a measuring jug will have the scale going vertically (up and down) rather than horizontally (from left to right).

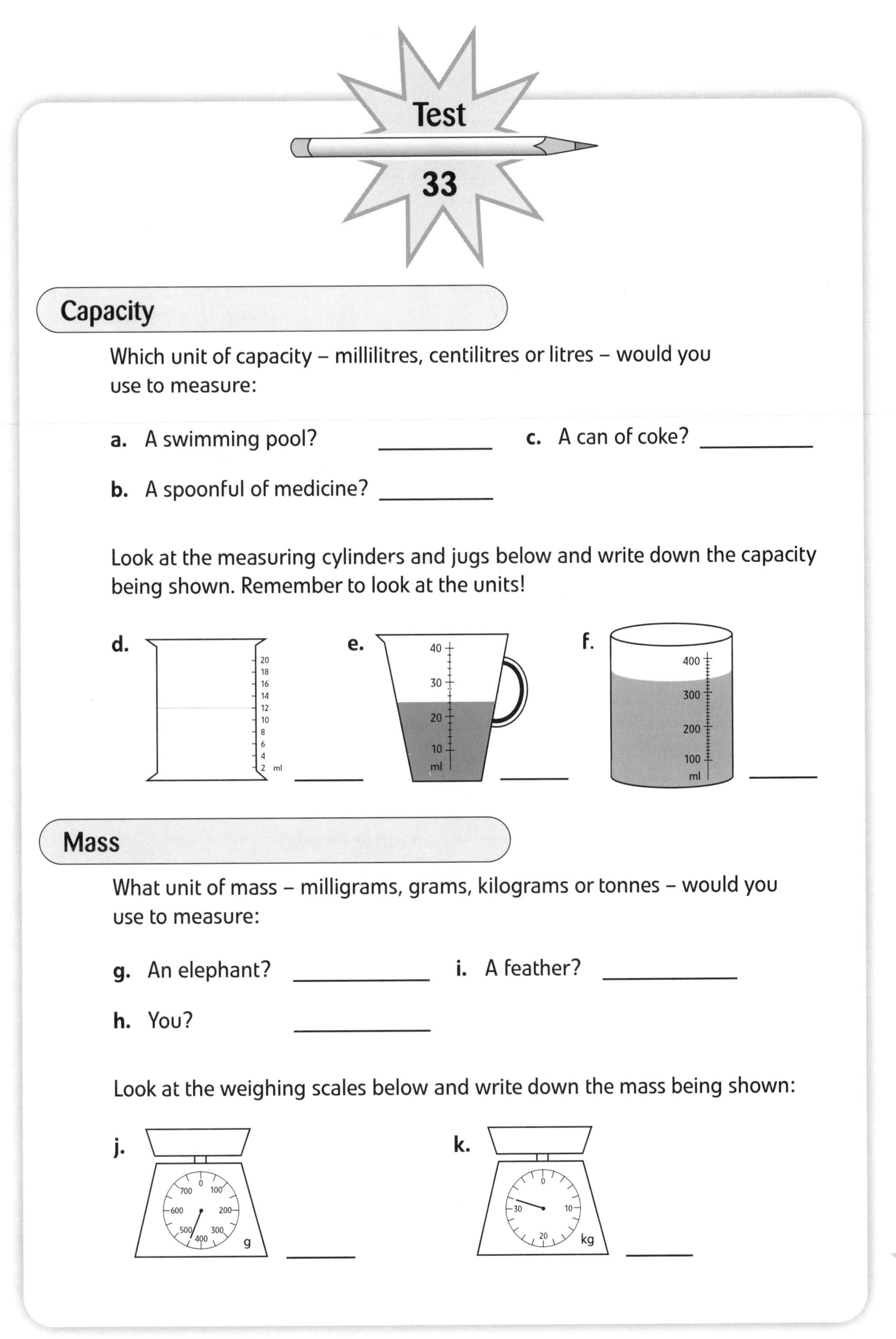

Test 33

Capacity

Which unit of capacity – millilitres, centilitres or litres – would you use to measure:

a. A swimming pool? __________

b. A spoonful of medicine? __________

c. A can of coke? __________

Look at the measuring cylinders and jugs below and write down the capacity being shown. Remember to look at the units!

d. ______ e. ______ f. ______

Mass

What unit of mass – milligrams, grams, kilograms or tonnes – would you use to measure:

g. An elephant? __________

h. You? __________

i. A feather? __________

Look at the weighing scales below and write down the mass being shown:

j. ______ k. ______

Time

What would our world be like without time? Everything that we do is measured by time – how old we are, when our birthday is, when our favourite TV programme is on and when school finishes.

Units of time

The problem with telling the time is that there are so many ways of doing it! Look at the following chart that shows the many units in which time is measured, starting with seconds:

60 seconds	**=**	**1 minute**	**365 days**	**=**	**1 year**
60 minutes	**=**	**1 hour**	**366 days**	**=**	**1 leap year**
24 hours	**=**	**1 day**	**10 years**	**=**	**1 decade**
7 days	**=**	**1 week**	**100 years**	**=**	**1 century**
14 days	**=**	**1 fortnight**	**1000 years**	**=**	**1 millennium**

A year can also be measured in weeks (52) and months (12).

Telling the time

We most commonly use watches and clocks to measure the passing of time. Analogue clocks and watches have hands that move around the face. The small hand points to the hour, and the large hand to the minutes. They work on a **12-hour system**, where ***a.m.*** means ***before midday*** and ***p.m.*** means ***after midday***.

The clock face has the numbers 1-12 to show the hours. The clock also has 60 minutes marked around the outside, with 1 showing 5 minutes, 2 showing 10 minutes and so on.

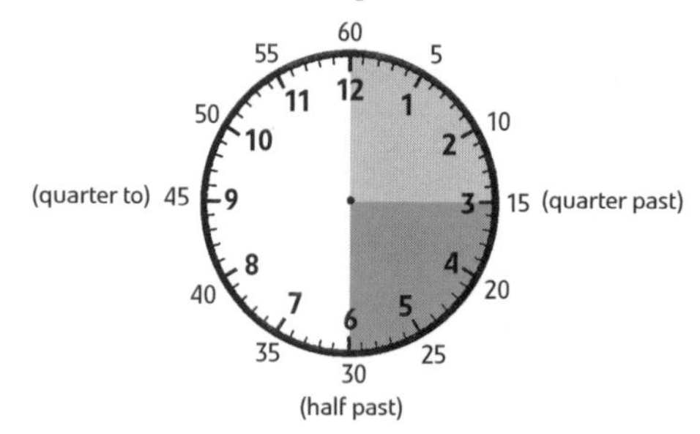

When the large hand points to the 12, we say ***'... o' clock'***.

When the large hand is between 12 and 6, we say ***'... minutes past'.***

When the large hand is on the 3, this is ***quarter past*** the hour.

When the large hand is on the 6, this is ***half past*** the hour.

Once the large hand is past the 6 we usually say ***'... minutes to'*** the next hour.

When the large hand is on the 9, this is ***quarter to*** the hour.

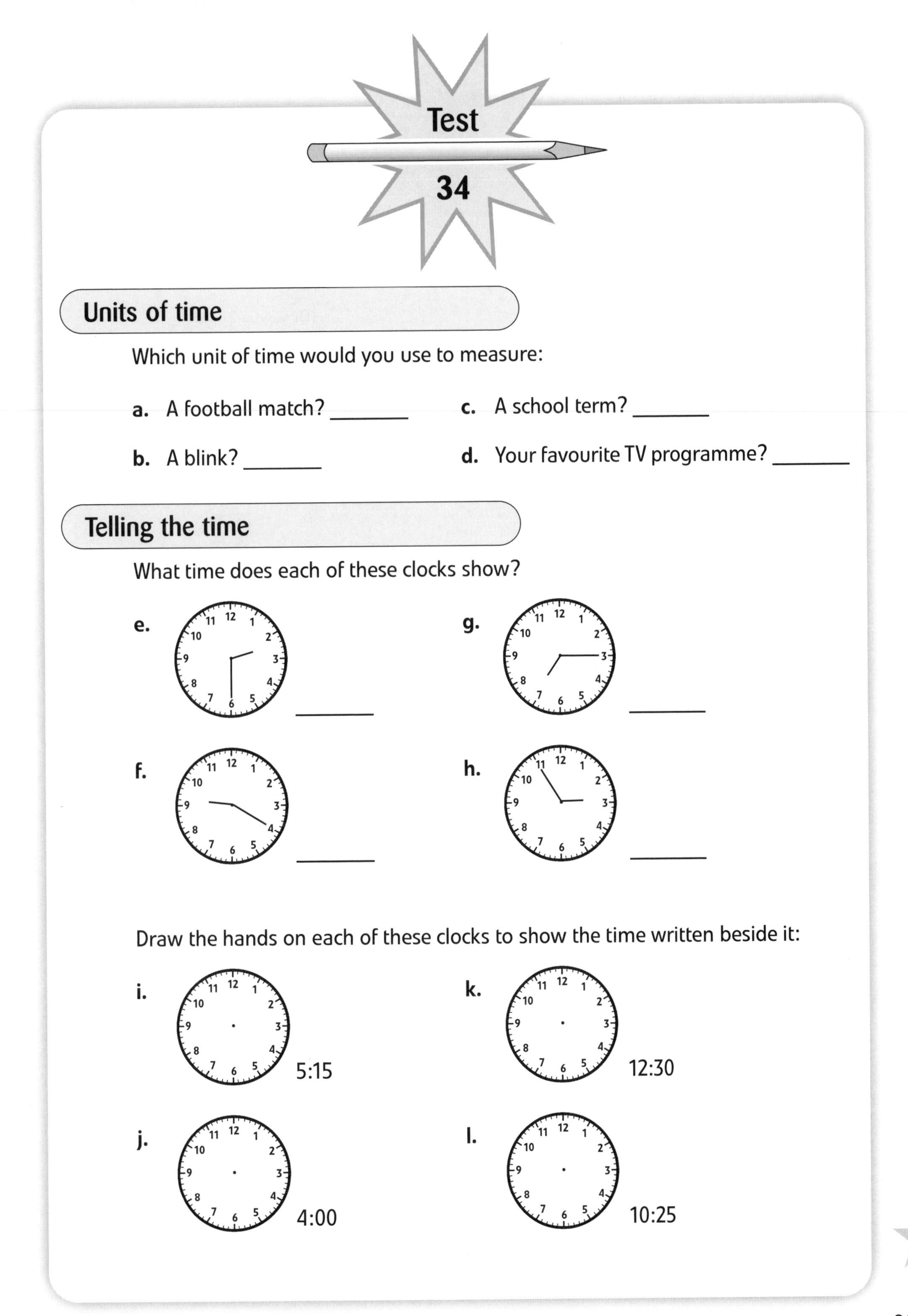

Test 34

Units of time

Which unit of time would you use to measure:

a. A football match? ________

b. A blink? ________

c. A school term? ________

d. Your favourite TV programme? ________

Telling the time

What time does each of these clocks show?

e. ________

f. ________

g. ________

h. ________

Draw the hands on each of these clocks to show the time written beside it:

i. 5:15

j. 4:00

k. 12:30

l. 10:25

Measures: Revision

Length 1

How many millimetres are in:

REMEMBER:

10mm = 1cm

100cm = 1m

1000m = 1km

a. 6cm ________

b. 10cm ________

c. 4cm ________

d. 9cm ________

e. $1\frac{1}{2}$cm ________

How many centimetres are in:

f. 110mm ________

g. 30mm ________

h. 240mm ________

i. 60mm ________

j. 350mm ________

How many centimetres are in:

k. 4m ________

l. 7m ________

m. 10m ________

n. 13m ________

o. 20m ________

p. $\frac{1}{2}$m ________

How many metres are in:

q. 6km ________

r. 10km ________

s. 8km ________

t. 15km ________

Length 2

Use a ruler to measure these lines:

a. ____ ☐ cm

b. ________________ ☐ cm

c. ________________________ ☐ cm

d. ____ ☐ cm

e. ________ ☐ cm

f. ______________________________________ ☐ cm

Now use your ruler to draw lines that are the following lengths:

g. 6cm

h. 10cm

i. 5cm

j. $6\frac{1}{2}$cm

k. 8cm

Measures: Revision

Capacity

a. How many millilitres are in a centilitre? ____________

b. How many centilitres are in a litre? ____________

c. How many millilitres are in a litre? ____________

d. How many millilitres are in $\frac{1}{2}$ litre? ____________

e. How many centilitres are in 3 litres? ____________

f. How many millilitres are in 5 litres? ____________

g. How many millilitres are in 6 centilitres? ____________

h. How many millilitres are in $7\frac{1}{2}$ litres? ____________

i. How many centilitres are in 10 litres? ____________

j. Jack poured 500ml of water into a bottle. He then added another 200ml. How many more millilitres does he need to add to make a litre?

____

k. Thomas had a litre bottle of coke. He poured out three cups each holding 50ml for his friends, and a cup for himself. How many millilitres were left in the bottle?

____

l. 10 buckets contain 1500ml of water altogether. How much in:

a) one bucket? __________ b) three buckets? __________

m. A baby has five bottles of milk a day, and each bottle holds 40ml of milk. How much milk does the baby drink in one day?

____

Mass

a. How many milligrams are in a gram? ______________

b. How many grams are in a kilogram? ______________

c. How many kilograms are in a tonne? ______________

d. How many milligrams are in a kilogram? ______________

e. How many kilograms in $\frac{1}{2}$ tonne? ______________

f. How many grams in $\frac{1}{4}$ kilogram? ______________

g. How many kilograms in 9 tonnes? ______________

h. How many milligrams in $3\frac{1}{2}$ grams? ______________

i. How many grams in 5 kilograms? ______________

j. Sarah went to the shops and weighed out 500g of bananas, 100g of grapes and 250g of apples. How much did the fruit weigh altogether?

____

k. David had three parcels weighed at the post office. The first was 400g, the second was 1kg and the third was 600g.

a) How much did the parcels weigh altogether?

____

b) If it costs £1.50 to send a parcel weighing $\frac{1}{2}$ kg, how much did it cost David to send his three parcels?

____

l. The ingredients for a cake are 200g of flour, 50g of butter and 100g of sugar. How much do these ingredients weigh altogether?

____

Measures: Revision

Time 1

a. How many seconds in a minute? ______

b. How many minutes in an hour? ______

c. How many hours in a day? ______

d. How many days in a week? ______

e. How many weeks in a year? ______

f. How many days in a year? ______

g. How many days in a leap year? ______

h. How many years in decade? ______

i. How many years in a century? ______

j. How many years in a millennium? ______

k. How many months in a year? ______

l. Two weeks can also be called a ______

m. What is the fifth month of the year? ______

n. What is the tenth month of the year? ______

o. What is the seventh month of the year? ______

p. What is the third month of the year? ______

q. What is the twelfth month of the year? ______

r. What is the second month of the year? ______

s. What is the eighth month of the year? ______

t. What are the four seasons of the year?

______ ______ ______ ______

Time 2

What time do these clocks show?

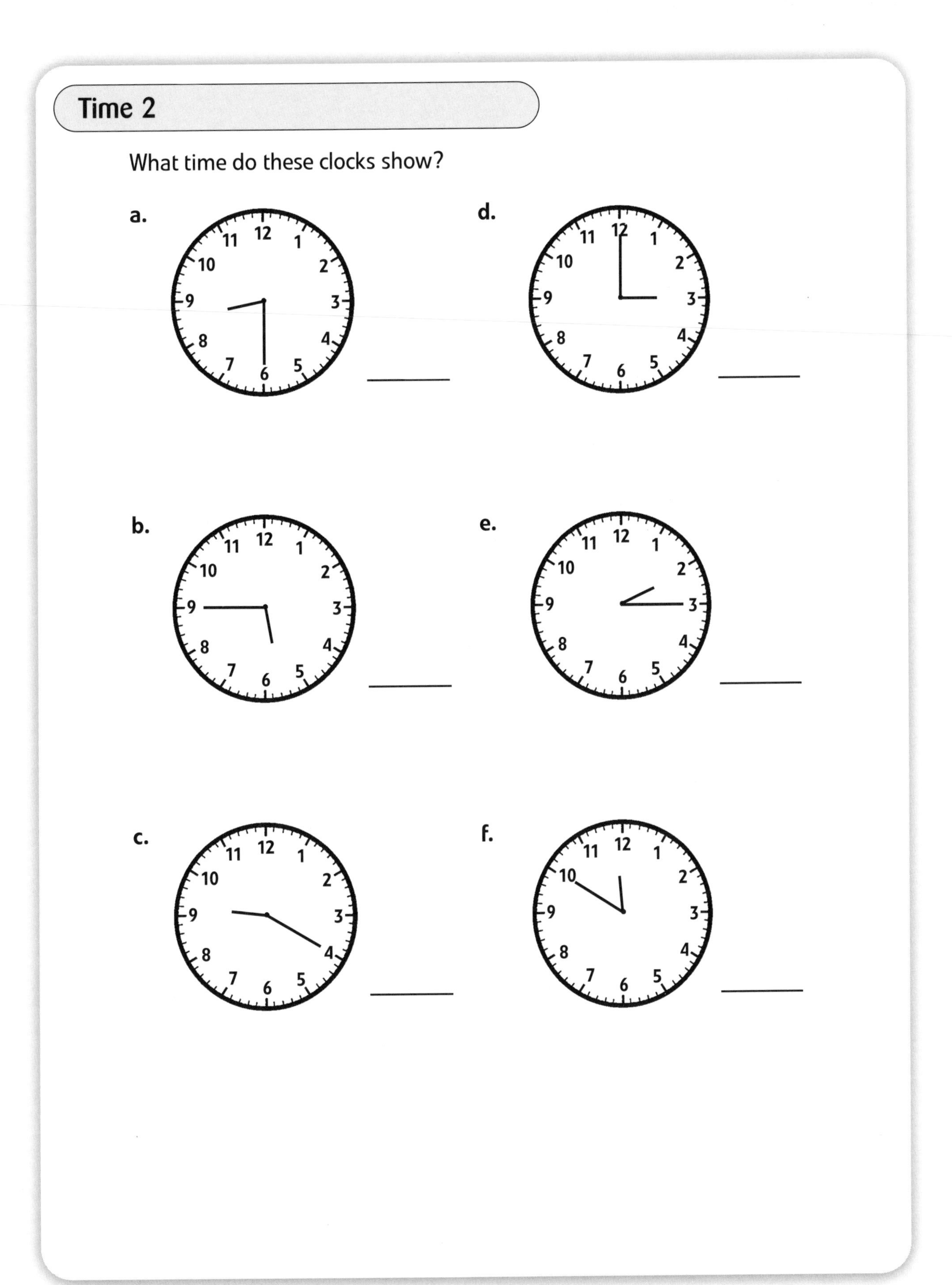

Measures: Revision

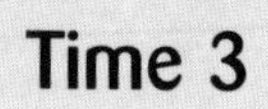

Time 3

Draw the hands on these clocks to show the times written beside them:

a.

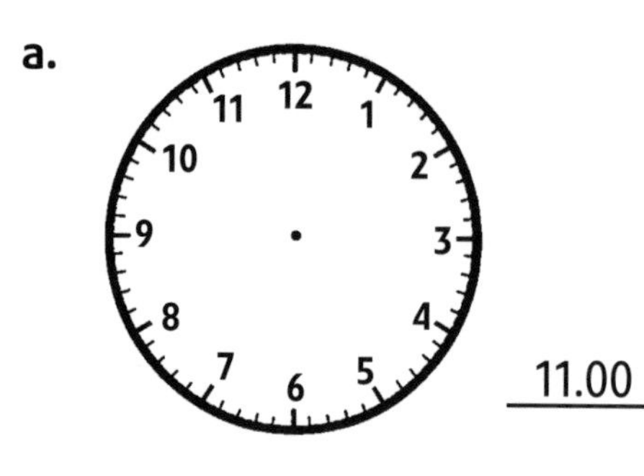

d.

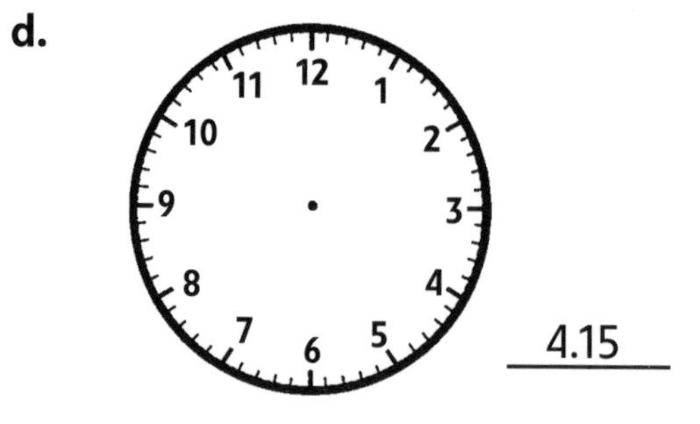

b.

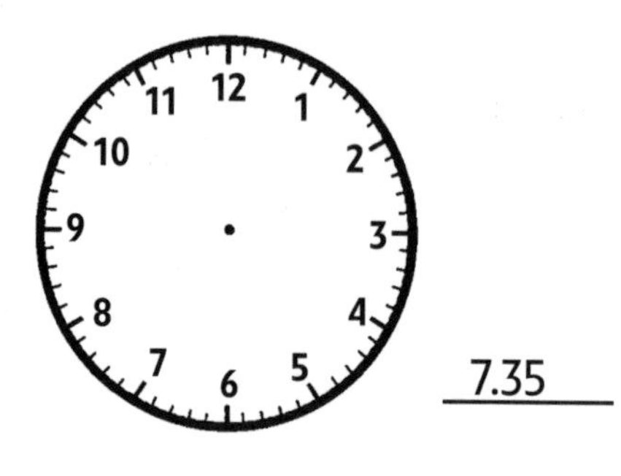

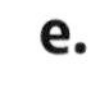

e.

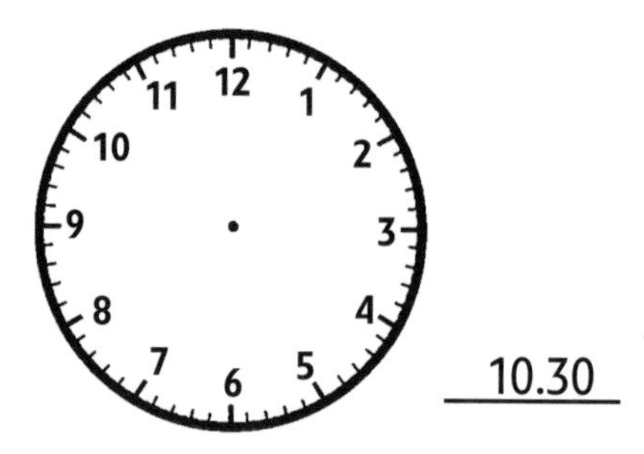

c.

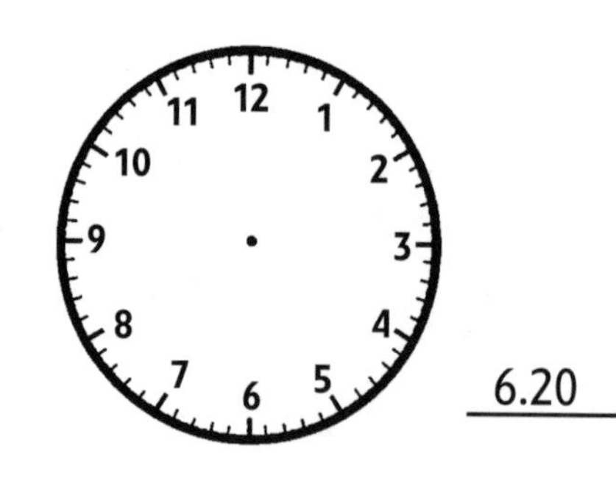

f.

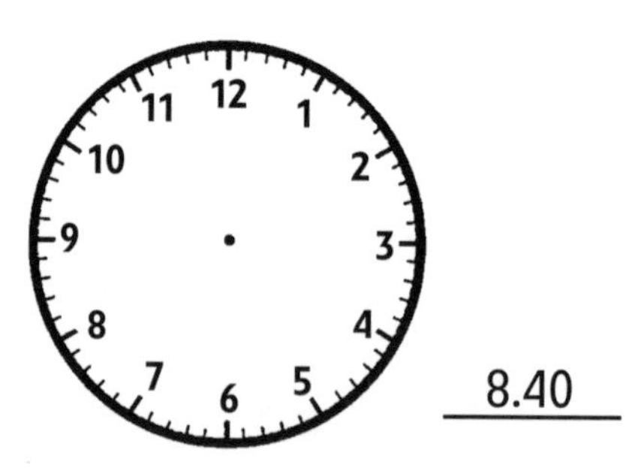

Time 4

Departure time	Arrival time				
London	Milton Keynes	Birmingham	Sheffield	Leeds	Glasgow
8.40am	10.00am	10.45am	11.00am	11.40am	2.40pm
9.30am	10.50am	11.35am	11.50am	12.30pm	3.30pm
10.15am	11.35am	12.20pm	12.35pm	1.15pm	4.15pm
12.00pm	**a?**	2.05pm	2.20pm	3.00pm	**b?**

Look at the train timetable above. Use the times of the other trains to calculate when the 12.00 train from London arrives in:

a. Milton Keynes ____________________

b. Glasgow ____________________

Use the timetable to answer the following questions:

c. What time does the 9.30 London train arrive in Birmingham? ________

d. What time does the 10.15 London train arrive in Sheffield? ________

e. How long does the train take to get from London to Leeds? ________

f. How long does the train take to get from London to Glasgow? ________

CHALLENGE!

If the 10.15 train from London was 15 minutes late, what time would the train arrive at each station?

Milton Keynes – ____________ Leeds – ____________

Birmingham – ____________ Glasgow – ____________

Sheffield – ____________

Glossary of terms

Analogue Analogue clocks and watches have hands that move round a face. They work on a 12-hour system, where a.m. means before midday and p.m. means after midday.

Area Area is the space occupied by 2-dimensional figures such as squares, triangles and circles.

Bar chart A bar chart is a diagram showing information in a way that is easy to understand. A bar chart looks like several blocks of flats standing near each other.

Capacity Capacity is a measure normally used for liquids such as petrol and milk.

Cone A cone is a circular pyramid in which the cross sections gradually diminish to a point.

Cube A cube is a 3-dimensional shape with 6 identical square faces.

Cuboid A cuboid is a 3-dimensional shape with 6 rectangular faces. A brick is a good example.

Cylinder A cylinder is a circular prism. Any slice of it is a circle. A good example is a Swiss roll.

Decimal A decimal indicates a part of something. Its written form uses a decimal point. So, 0.1 indicates one tenth.

Denominator
A denominator is the bottom number in a fraction. So, in $\frac{3}{4}$ the denominator is 4. The top number is the numerator.

Digit A digit is a single numeral (0, 1, 2 ... 9) used to represent part of a number in a place value system.

Doubling To multiply a number by 2, or by adding it to itself.

Equilateral triangle
An equilateral triangle has 3 equal sides and 3 equal angles.

Even A number that can be divided equally by 2 is called an even number.

Factor A factor is a number that divides exactly into another number.

Fraction A fraction is a part of something. The most common fraction is a half, written as $\frac{1}{2}$.

Halving To divide a number by 2.

Heptagon A heptagon is a 7-sided 2-dimensional figure. A 50p coin is the shape of a heptagon.

Hexagon A hexagon is a 6-sided 2-dimensional figure.

Line of symmetry A line of symmetry cuts a shape into 2 equal halves, so that if the paper is folded along the line of symmetry, the 2 halves will fit exactly on top of one another.

Multiple A multiple is the result of multiplying one number by another. Some multiples of 4 are 8, 12, 24, 28.

Numeral A numeral is a symbol used to denote a number.

Numerator A numerator is the top number in a fraction. So, in $\frac{3}{4}$ the numerator is 3. The bottom number is the denominator.

Glossary of terms

Octagon An octagon is an 8-sided 2-dimensional figure.

Odd A number that cannot be divided equally by 2 is called an odd number.

Partitioning To split a number to show the separate value of its digits.

Pentagon A pentagon is a 5-sided 2-dimensional figure.

Place value Place value is the value of a digit according to its place in a number. In 104 the digit 1 has a value of 100, but in 215 the digit 1 has a value of 10.

Polygon A polygon is a 2-dimensional shape made of 3 or more straight lines.

Quadrilateral A quadrilateral is a 4-sided 2-dimensional figure. Examples include: kite, parallelogram, rhombus and trapezium.

Rectangle A rectangle is a quadrilateral with 4 right angles.

Reflective symmetry Reflective symmetry refers to a shape where 2 halves are perfect mirror images of each other.

Rounding Rounding means expressing a number approximately rather than precisely.

Symmetry *See Line of symmetry and Reflective symmetry.*

Triangle A triangle is a 3-sided 2-dimensional figure.

Hundred Square

1	2	3	4	5	6	7	8	9	10
11	12	13	14	15	16	17	18	19	20
21	22	23	24	25	26	27	28	29	30
31	32	33	34	35	36	37	38	39	40
41	42	43	44	45	46	47	48	49	50
51	52	53	54	55	56	57	58	59	60
61	62	63	64	65	66	67	68	69	70
71	72	73	74	75	76	77	78	79	80
81	82	83	84	85	86	87	88	89	90
91	92	93	94	95	96	97	98	99	100

Multiplication Table

1	2	3	4	5	6	7	8	9	10
2	4	6	8	10	12	14	16	18	20
3	6	9	12	15	18	21	24	27	30
4	8	12	16	20	24	28	32	36	40
5	10	15	20	25	30	35	40	45	50
6	12	18	24	30	36	42	48	54	60
7	14	21	28	35	42	49	56	63	70
8	16	24	32	40	48	56	64	72	80
9	18	27	36	45	54	63	72	81	90
10	20	30	40	50	60	70	80	90	100

Answers

Test 1

a. 60 or 6 tens
b. 9 or 9 units
c. 70 or 7 tens
d. 100 or 1 hundred
e. 0 or 0 tens
f. 40 or 4 tens
g. 2 or 2 units
h. 50 or 5 tens
i. 800 or 8 hundreds
j. 90 or 9 tens
k. 1 or 1 unit
l. 400 or 4 hundreds
m. 853
n. 358
o. 358 or 385
p. 538, 583, 835, 853

Test 2

a. 60 and 2
b. 10 and 2
c. 30 and 0
d. 50 and 8
e. 70 and 9
f. 80 and 4
g. 400 and 20 and 9
h. 600 and 30 and 2
i. 300 and 00 and 5
j. 200 and 20 and 2
k. 96
l. 42
m. 68
n. 332
o. 958
p. 461

Test 3

a. 30
b. 30
c. 60
d. 80
e. 10
f. 130
g. 660
h. 710
i. $>$
j. $>$
k. $<$
l. $>$
m. $<$
n. $<$
o. T
p. F
q. T
r. F
s. T
t. T

Test 4

a. 7
b. 2
c. 6
d. 9
e. 0
f. 5
g. 10
h. 8
i. 7
j. 5
k. 9
l. 6
m. 8
n. 2
o. 30
p. 50

Answers

q. 30
r. 40
s. 70
t. 90
u. 3
v. 6
w. 18
x. 8
y. 14
z. 1

Test 5

a.
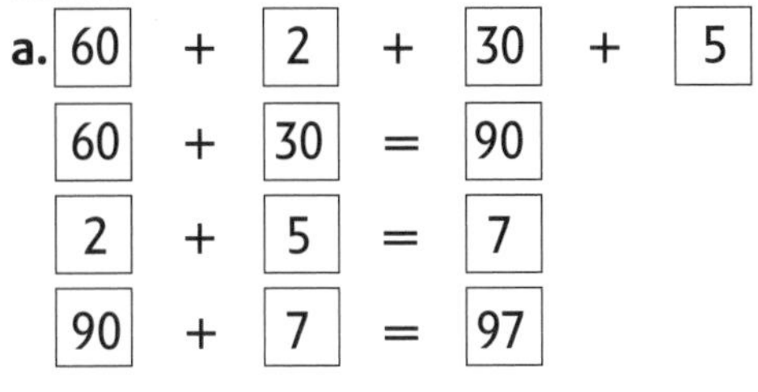

b. 79
c. 93
d. 92
e. 78
f. 88
g. 76
h. 366
i. 655
j. 886
k. 772

Test 6

a.
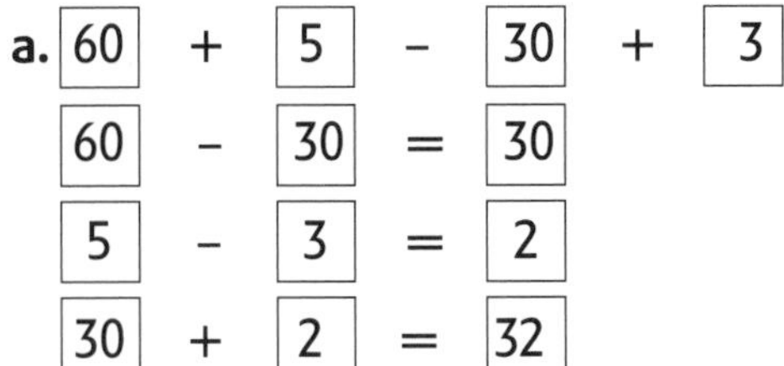

b. 36
c. 13
d. 6
e. 42
f. 51
g. 17
h. 18
i. 17

Test 7

a. 55
b. 79
c. 59
d. 99
e. 150
f. 269

Test 8

Set A		Set B
3	–	6
4	–	8
6	–	12
8	–	16
12	–	24
15	–	30
17	–	34
22	–	44
50	–	100
120	–	240
310	–	620
400	–	800

a. 32
b. 120
c. 56
d. 164
e. 48
f. 100
g. 440

Answers

h. 600
i. 5
j. 8
k. 10
l. 25
m. 50
n. 100
o. 5
p. 10
q. 12
r. 15
s. 25
t. 105

Test 9

a. 10, 12, 14, 16, 18, 20
b. 25, 30, 35, 40, 45, 50
c. 15, 18, 21, 24, 27, 30
d. 20, 24, 28, 32, 36, 40

Test 10

a. 12, 24 – 12 = 12
b. 25, 39 – 14 = 25
c. 26, 43 – 17 = 26
d. 17, 26 – 9 = 17
e. 31, 58 – 27 = 31
f. 35, 98 – 63 = 35
g. 30, 57 – 27 = 30
h. 4, 28 ÷ 7 = 4
i. 5, 15 ÷ 3 = 5
j. 7, 35 ÷ 5 = 7
k. 12, 24 ÷ 2 = 12
l. 4, 40 ÷ 10 = 4
m. 8, 32 ÷ 4 = 8
n. 5, 55 ÷ 11 = 5
o. 7 + 19 = 26, 19 + 7 = 26,
26 – 7 = 19, 26 – 19 = 7
p. 13 + 14 = 27, 14 + 13 = 27,
27 – 13 = 14, 27 – 14 = 13
q. 23 + 37 = 60, 37 + 23 = 60,
60 – 23 = 37, 60 – 37 = 23
r. 42 + 51 = 93, 51 + 42 = 93,
93 – 42 = 51, 93 – 51 = 42
s. 5 x 10 = 50, 10 x 5 = 50,
50 ÷ 5 = 10, 50 ÷ 10 = 5
t. 2 x 4 = 8, 4 x 2 = 8,
8 ÷ 2 = 4, 8 ÷ 4 = 2
u. 3 x 9 = 27, 9 x 3 = 27,
27 ÷ 3 = 9, 27 ÷ 9 = 3
v. 5 x 4 = 20, 4 x 5 =20,
20 ÷ 5 = 4, 20 ÷ 4 = 5

Test 11

a. Practise = 65
b. 60
c. 36
d. 63
e. 45
f. 780
g. 93
h. 225
i. 144
j. Practise = 502
k. 369
l. 272
m. 1160
n. 2100

Test 12

a. 30 ÷ 6 = 5 or 30 ÷ 5 = 6
b. 16 ÷ 2 = 8 or 16 ÷ 8 = 2
c. 35 ÷ 7 = 5 or 35 ÷ 5 = 7
d. 50 ÷ 10 = 5 or 50 ÷ 5 = 10
e. 9
f. 6
g. 3
h. 6
i. 5
j. 25
k. 2
l. 12
m. 16

Answers

Test 13

a. 630
b. 170
c. 420
d. 910
e. 370
f. 1320

Set A		Set B
3	–	30
7	–	70
21	–	210
6	–	60
4	–	40
11	–	110
2	–	20
1	–	10
9	–	90
33	–	330
62	–	620
90	–	900

g. 400
h. 700
i. 1800
j. 2200
k. 3800
l. 7200
m. To multiply a number by 10, move all its digits **one** place to the **left**.
n. To multiply a number by 100, move all its digits **two** places to the **left**.

Test 14

a. 6
b. 7
c. 3
d. 63
e. 35
f. 89

Set A		Set B
340	–	34
120	–	12
90	–	9
560	–	56
40	–	4
310	–	31
990	–	99
100	–	10
400	–	40
730	–	73

g. 4
h. 9
i. 3
j. 32
k. 99
l. 41
m. To divide a number by 10, move all its digits **one** place to the **right**.
n. To divide a number by 100, move all its digits **two** places to the **right**.

Test 15

a. 5, 7, 9, 11, 13, 15
b. 27, 29, 31, 33, 35, 37
c. 63, 65, 67, 69, 71, 73
d. 6, 8, 10, 12, 14, 16
e. 24, 26, 28, 30, 32, 34
f. 80, 82, 84, 86, 88, 90
g. 12, 15, 30, 6, 33
h. Any whole number ending in 0 or 5.
i. 1, 3, 5, 15
j. 1, 2, 4, 5, 10, 20
k. 1, 2, 3, 4, 6, 9, 12, 18, 36
l. 1, 2, 3, 6, 9, 18
m. 90, 95 (increasing by 5)
n. 22, 26 (increasing by 4)
o. 18, 16 (decreasing by 2)

Answers

Test 16

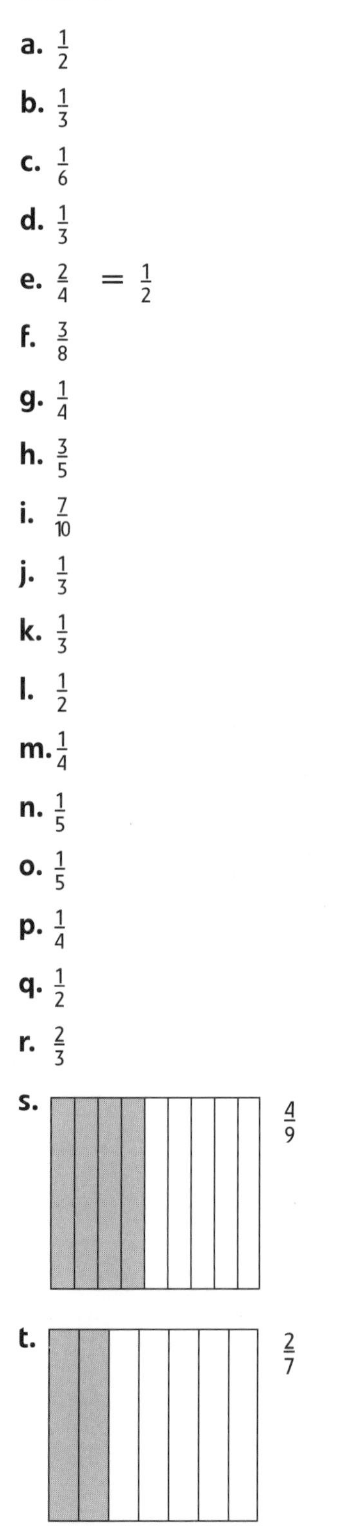

a. $\frac{1}{2}$

b. $\frac{1}{3}$

c. $\frac{1}{6}$

d. $\frac{1}{3}$

e. $\frac{2}{4} = \frac{1}{2}$

f. $\frac{3}{8}$

g. $\frac{1}{4}$

h. $\frac{3}{5}$

i. $\frac{7}{10}$

j. $\frac{1}{3}$

k. $\frac{1}{3}$

l. $\frac{1}{2}$

m. $\frac{1}{4}$

n. $\frac{1}{5}$

o. $\frac{1}{5}$

p. $\frac{1}{4}$

q. $\frac{1}{2}$

r. $\frac{2}{3}$

s. $\frac{4}{9}$

t. $\frac{2}{7}$

u. 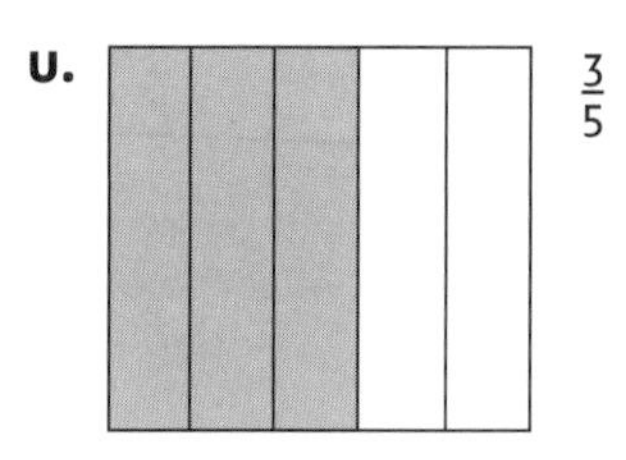 $\frac{3}{5}$

Test 17

a. 8

b. 6

c. 6

d. 14

e. 16

f. 3

g. 4

h. 10

i. 39

j. 10

k. 18

l. 2

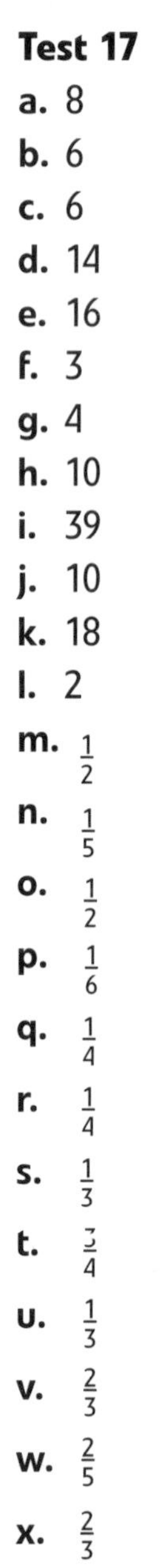

m. $\frac{1}{2}$

n. $\frac{1}{5}$

o. $\frac{1}{2}$

p. $\frac{1}{6}$

q. $\frac{1}{4}$

r. $\frac{1}{4}$

s. $\frac{1}{3}$

t. $\frac{3}{4}$

u. $\frac{1}{3}$

v. $\frac{2}{3}$

w. $\frac{2}{5}$

x. $\frac{2}{3}$

Answers

Test 18

a. 12.7
b. 8.9
c. 32.5
d. 31.05
e. 28.02
f. 19.12
g. 17.8
h. 80.09
i. twelve point four
j. eight point zero six
k. forty one point six
l. fifteen point one
m. nine point seven
n. three hundred and two point five
o. thirty one point one two
p. fourteen point zero nine
q. ninety eight point one one
r. seventy one point three
s. 0.3
t. 0.3
u. 1.4
v. 3.8
w. 12.9
x. 14.8
y. 3.2, 3.5, 3.62, 3.7, 3.75, 3.9

Test 19

a. 5p, 2p, 1p, or 2p, 2p, 2p, 2p, or 1p, 1p, 1p, 1p, 1p, 1p, 1p, 1p etc
b. 10p, 2p or 5p, 5p, 2p etc
c. 10p, 5p or 5p, 5p, 5p etc
d. 20p, 2p, 1p or 10p, 10p, 1p, 1p, 1p etc
e. 50p, 20p, 20p, 5p, 2p, 1p etc
f. £0.89
g. £0.98
h. £1.07
i. £3.10
j. £5.02
k. £2.05
l. 55p
m. 20p
n. 71p
o. 21p
p. 89p
q. 16p
r. 69p or £0.69
s. 108p or £1.08
t. 132p or £1.32
u. 161p or £1.61
v. 321p or £3.21
w. 85p or £0.85

Test 20

a. Hut
b. Tree
c. Treasure
d. Boat
e. Mountains
f. Windmill
g. Shark
h. Bridge
i. A5
j. B2
k. D4
l. B2
m. E4
n. D4
o. B2
p. A1

UNDERSTANDING NUMBERS: REVISION

Place value

a 30 or 3 tens
b. 6 or 6 units
c. 2
d. 4
e. 0

Answers

f. 1
g. 865
h. 1357
i. 136, 163, 316, 361, 613, 631

Partitioning

a. 70 and 2
b. 80 and 3
c. 100 and 20 and 3
d. 600 and 20 and 2
e. 1000 and 50 and 2
f. 49
g. 62
h. 409
i. 1357

Rounding, greater than and less than

a. 70
b. 30
c. 80
d. 80
e. 100
f. 350
g. 870
h. 1070
i. No
j. Yes
k. No
l. Yes
m. Yes
n. No
o. Yes
p. Yes

Number pairs that total 10 and 20

a. 4
b. 9
c. 7
d. 0
e. 1
f. 8
g. 5
h. 3
i. 15
j. 12
k. 4
l. 11
m. 8
n. 16
o. 6
p. 15

Addition using partitioning

a. 38
b. 49
c. 30
d. 49
e. 58
f. 61
g. 117
h. 87
i. 107
j. 178
k. 287
l. 369

Subtraction using partitioning

a. 44
b. 34
c. 20
d. 33
e. 41
f. 26

Subtraction using a number line

a. 22
b. 25
c. 17

Answers

d. 68
e. 36
f. 114

Counting on in tens and units

a. 103
b. 80
c. 83
d. 201
e. 183
f. 290
g. 584

Doubling and halving

a. 12
b. 10
c. 18
d. 24
e. 64
f. 80
g. 130
h. 248
i. 116
j. 126
k. £16.00
l. 36cm
m. 24
n. 48
o. 96
p. 3
q. 5
r. 11
s. 24
t. 48
u. 50
v. 225
w. £2.50
x. 19cm

Multiplication tables

a. 18
b. 28
c. 9
d. 8
e. 35
f. 30
g. 20
h. 30
i. 15, 18, 21
j. 40, 35, 30
k. 14, 16, 18
l. 40, 50, 60

Inverse operations

a. $7 + 5 = 12$, $5 + 7 = 12$,
$12 - 7 = 5$, $12 - 5 = 7$
b. $3 + 1 = 4$, $1 + 3 = 4$,
$4 - 1 = 3$, $4 - 3 = 1$
c. $6 \times 4 = 24$, $4 \times 6 = 24$,
$24 \div 6 = 4$, $24 \div 4 = 6$
d. $5 \times 3 = 15$, $3 \times 5 = 15$,
$15 \div 5 = 3$, $15 \div 3 = 5$
e. $10 \times 10 = 100$, $100 \div 10 = 10$
f. $6 + 3 = 9$, $3 + 6 = 9$,
$9 - 3 = 6$, $9 - 6 = 3$
g. $12 + 12 = 24$, $24 - 12 = 12$
h. $2 \times 8 = 16$, $8 \times 2 = 16$,
$16 \div 2 = 8$, $16 \div 8 = 2$
i. $14 + 16 = 30$, $16 + 14 = 30$,
$30 - 16 = 14$, $30 - 14 = 16$
j. $20 + 80 = 100$, $80 + 20 = 100$,
$100 - 80 = 20$, $100 - 20 = 80$

Multiplication with larger numbers

a. 80
b. 72
c. 63

Answers

d. 225
e. 252
f. 375
g. 805
h. 370
i. 964
j. 936
k. 1350

Division
a. 9
b. 4
c. 9
d. 10
e. 4
f. 4
g. 24
h. 25
i. 100
j. 11
k. 8
l. 12
m. 10
n. 9
o. 40
p. 7

Multiplying and dividing by 10 and 100
a. 60
b. 120
c. 420
d. 810
e. 4570
f. 3460
g. 900
h. 1600
i. 2800
j. 45300
k. 62800

l. 7
m. 9
n. 12
o. 22
p. 1
q. 16
r. 84
s. 104
t. 45

Fabulous facts
a. 1, 2, 3, 6
b. 1, 2, 3, 4, 6, 12
c. 1, 3, 5, 7 or 9
d. 28, 30, 32 or 34
e. 33, 36, 39
f. 40, 36, 32

Fractions of numbers
a. 6
b. 5
c. 10
d. 6
e. 2
f. 5
g. $\frac{1}{2}$
h. $\frac{1}{4}$
i. $\frac{1}{4}$
j. $\frac{1}{2}$

Decimals
a. 7 or 7 units
b. 0.3 or 3 tenths
c. 0.09 or 9 hundredths
d. 0.05, 0.12, 0.2, 0.6
e. 12.09, 12.5, 12.7, 12.8

Answers

Money

a. £0.89
b. £3.45
c. £2.30
d. £2.08
e. £17.35
f. 170p
g. 190p
h. 76p
i. 7p
j. 1234p

Coordinates and compass points

a-d.

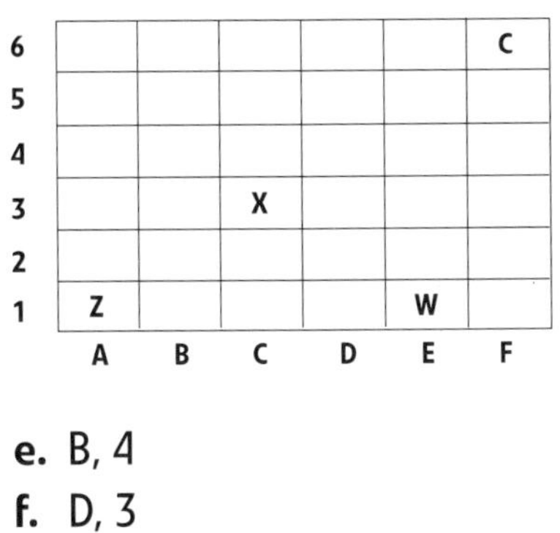

e. B, 4
f. D, 3
g. E, 6
h. A, 2

Test 21

a.

b.

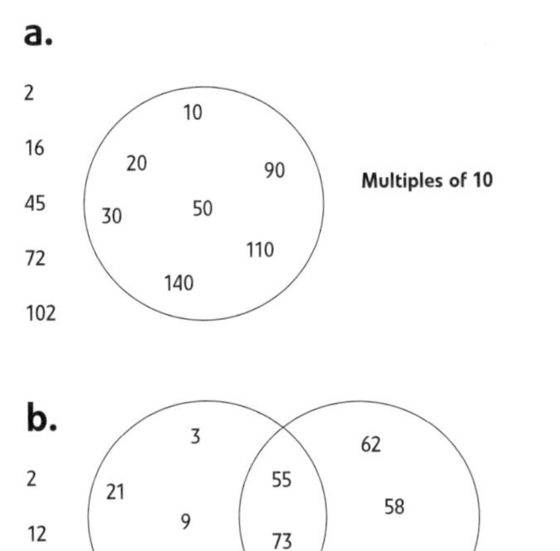

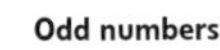

c.

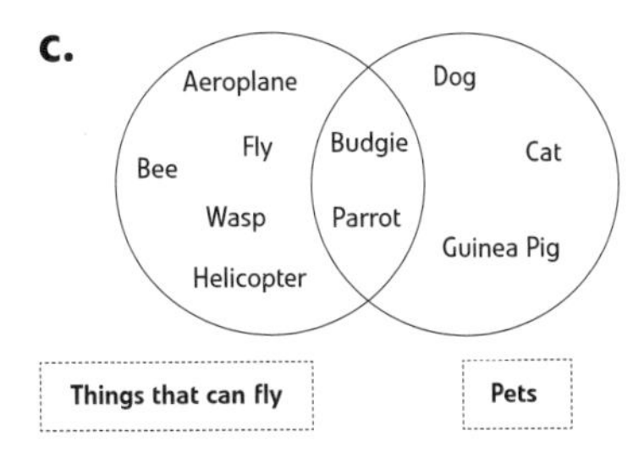

Test 22

a.

Factors of 100	Not factors of 100
2	7
4	15
5	30
10	32
20	33
25	36
50	40
100	51
	90

b.

	Factors of 100	Not factors of 100
Odd numbers	5 25	7 15 33 51
Not odd numbers	2 4 10 20 50 100	30 32 36 40 90

c.

	Breakfast foods	Not breakfast foods
Meat	Sausages Bacon	Pork chop Chicken kiev Mince beef Corned beef
Not meat	Egg Tomatoes Cereal Mushrooms Milk Bread Jam	Cake Pasta Pizza

Answers

Test 23

a. 3
b. Purple
c. Red
d. Pink
e. Cats
f. Fish, Other
g. 10
h. 25

Test 24

a. Tally Chart

Age of passengers	Tally	Total
Under 25	𝍸 𝍸 𝍸 𝍸 𝍸 III	28
26-39	𝍸 𝍸 II	12
40-59	𝍸 𝍸 𝍸 III	18
60+	𝍸 𝍸 𝍸 𝍸 𝍸 𝍸 III	33

b. Bar Chart

Number of people

0 5 10 15 20 25 30 35

Under 25 | 26 to 39 | 40 to 59 | 60+

Ages

Test 25

a. Frequency table

Letters in name	Number of children
3 letters	5
4 letters	6
5 letters	10
6+ letters	3

b. Bar chart

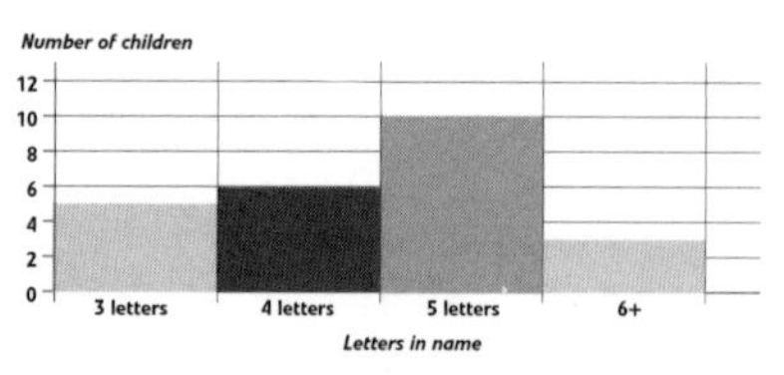

Test 26

a. 2
b. $1\frac{1}{2}$
c. Sunday
d. Monday, Thursday
e. Class 3
f. Class 2
g. 25
h. Class 2
i. Class 3

HANDLING DATA: REVISION

Venn diagrams

a.

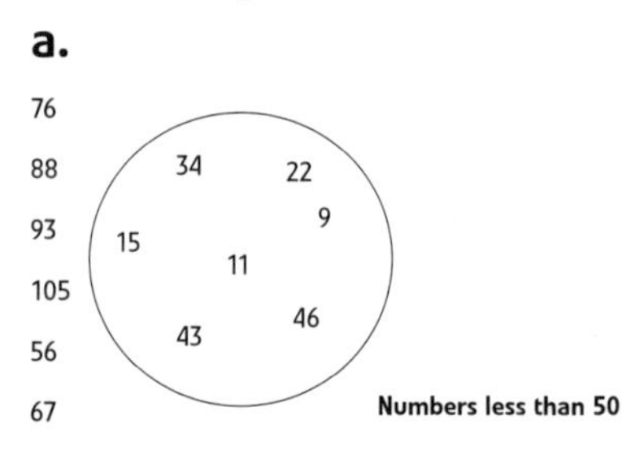

b.

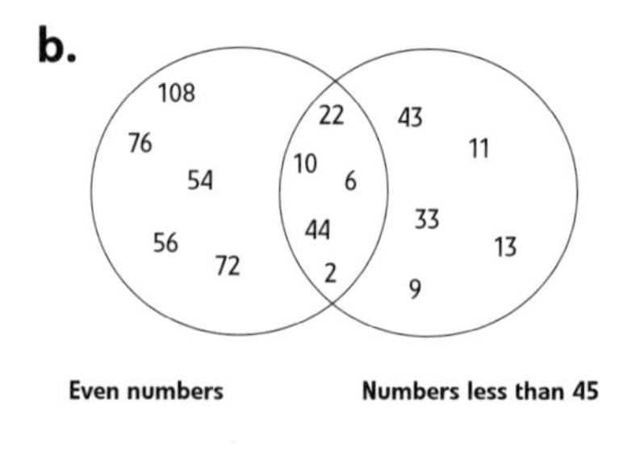

Venn diagrams 2

a.

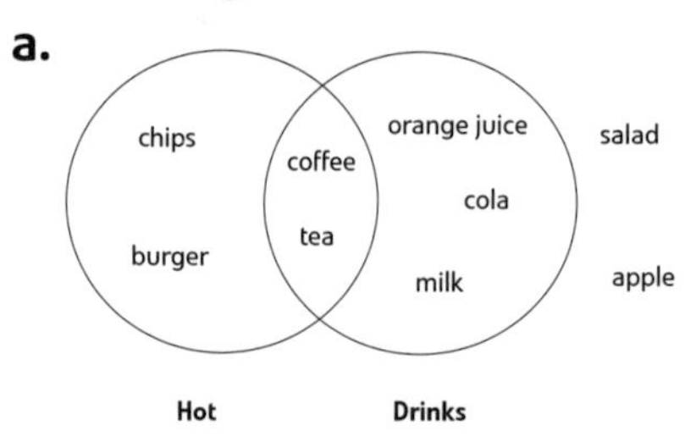

b. 'Multiples of 3' and 'Numbers less than 50'

Answers

Carroll diagrams 1

a.

Multiples of 5	Not multiples of 5
35	24
105	11
45	98
80	37
25	7
225	52
15	192

b.

	Multiples of 5	Not Multiples of 5
Even numbers	80	24 98 52 192
Not even numbers	35 105 45 25 225 15	11 37 7

Carroll diagrams 2

a.

A sport using a ball	A sport not using a ball
Netball	Swimming
Football	Running
Basketball	Skiing
Tennis	Gymnastics
Rugby	Motor racing

b.

	Mammals	Not mammals
Live in the sea	Whales Dolphins Seals Walrus	Shark Octopus
Do not live in the sea	Monkeys Humans Tigers	Tortoise Blackbird Butterfly

Bar charts

a. 14
b. Guinea pig
c. 39
d. Cat and rabbit
e. 8
f. Ball
g. Train – 9
Doll – 7
Skipping rope – 4

Tally charts

a.

Type of letter	Tally	Total
Vowel	卌 卌 卌 ||||	19
Consonant	卌 卌 卌 卌 卌 卌 卌 卌	40

b. Appropriate tally chart

Drawing bar charts

a.

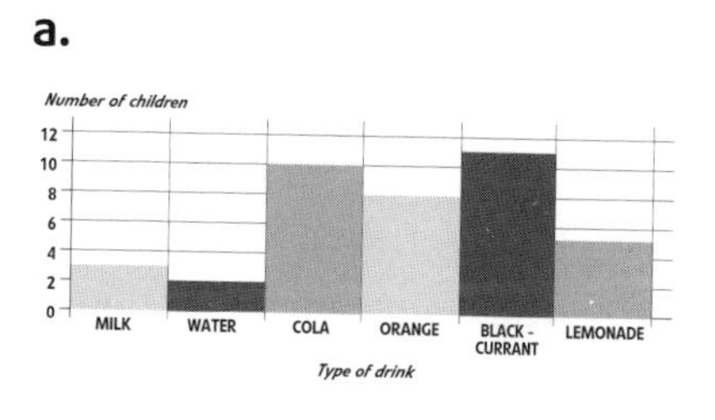

b. Totals

Blackbird = 8
Sparrow = 16
Bluetit = 6
Chaffinch = 3
Unknown = 9

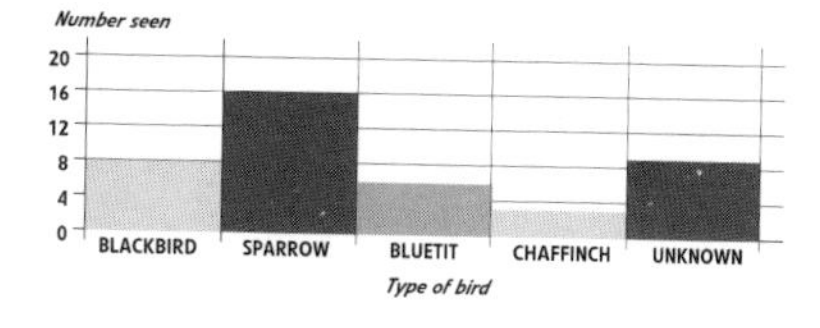

Answers

Frequency tables

Type of fruit	Amount of fruit
Oranges	10
Bananas	20
Apples	30
Grapes	15

Pictograms

a. 3

b. 3

c. Thursday

d. 29

e. People are not at work or school on a Saturday, so more television can be watched

Test 27

a. Triangle

b. Square

c. Hexagon

d. Octagon

e. Pentagon

f. Heptagon

g. Rectangle

h. 8 sides, 8 angles

i. 6 sides, the same length

j-m. Any suitably shaped object is acceptable

Test 28

a. Cuboid

b. Cone

c. Square-based pyramid

d. Triangular prism

e. Sphere

f. Cylinder

g. 6 faces, square

h. 4 faces, triangular

i. 1

j. 9

k-n. Any suitably shaped object is acceptable

Test 29

a.

b.

c.

d.

e.

f.

g.

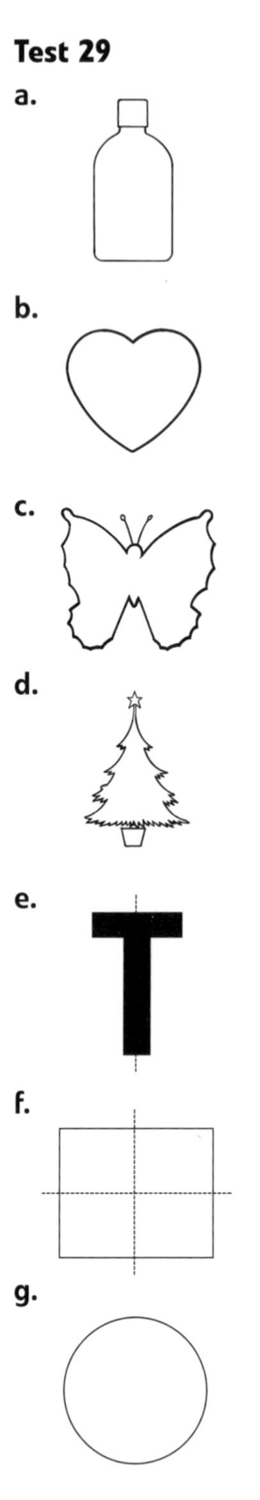

Any number of lines through the middle point.

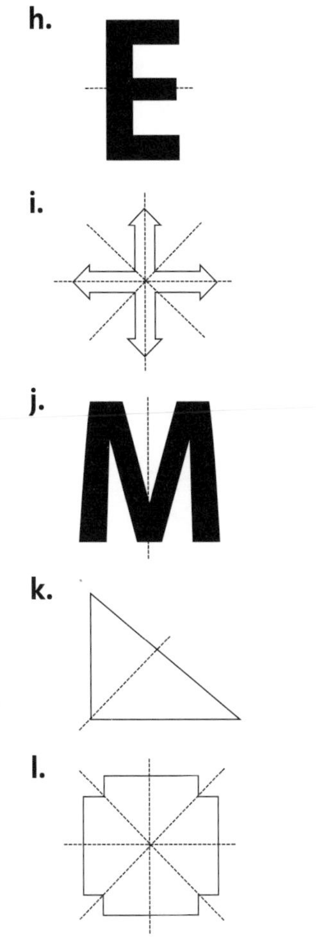

Test 30

a. $12cm^2$
b. $8cm^2$
c. $14cm^2$
d. $12cm^2$
e. $16cm^2$
f. $24cm^2$
g. $100cm^2$ or $1m^2$

Test 31

a. 22cm
b. 16cm
c. 30cm
d. 20.5cm

GEOMETRY: REVISION

Polygons

a. Triangle
b. Rectangle
c. Pentagon
d. Hexagon
e. Triangle
f. Hexagon
g. Hexagon
h. Quadrilateral

Properties of shapes

a. 3
b. 7
c. Octagon
d. True
e. Square
f. Hexagon
g. Equilateral triangle
h. Rectangle

Drawing shapes

a.

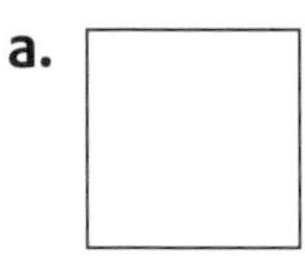

b. Any two triangles are acceptable

c.

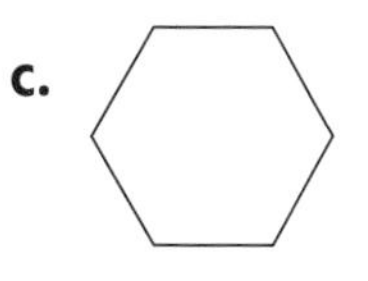

d. Any three shapes are acceptable

Answers

3-D Shapes

a. Length, width, height
b. 6
c. Square
d. None
e. Triangle and rectangle
f. Cuboid
g. Sphere
h.

3-D Shape	Number of faces	Number of vertices	Number of edges
Cube	6	8	12
Cuboid	6	8	12
Cone	2	1	1
Triangular prism	5	6	9
Tetrahedron	4	4	6
Cylinder	3	0	2

i. Appropriate tally chart

Symmetry

a.

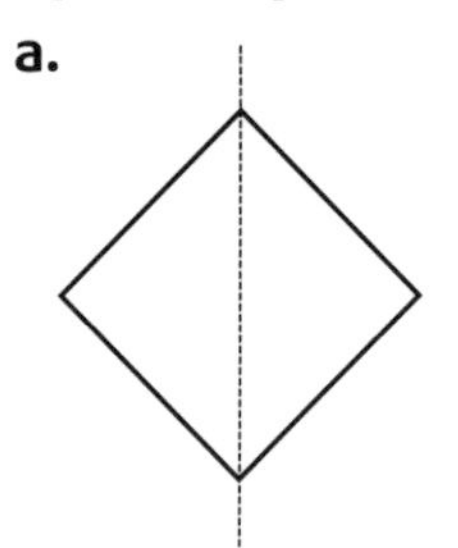

b.

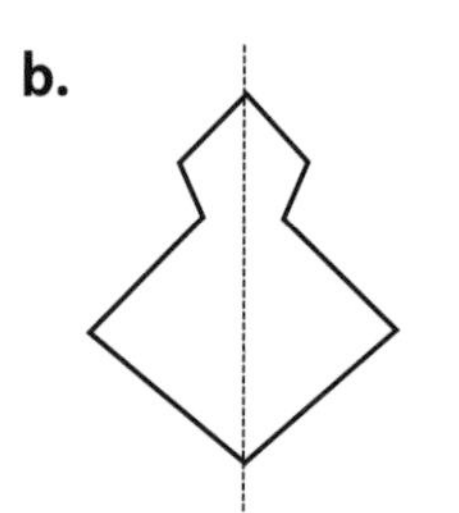

c.

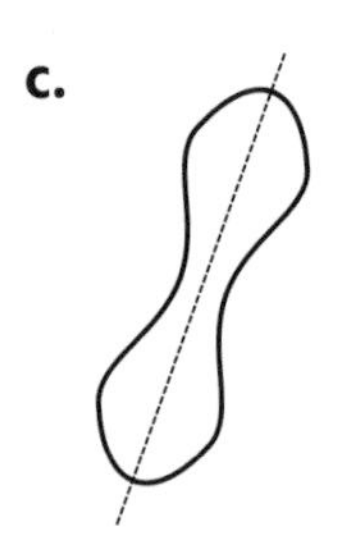

d.

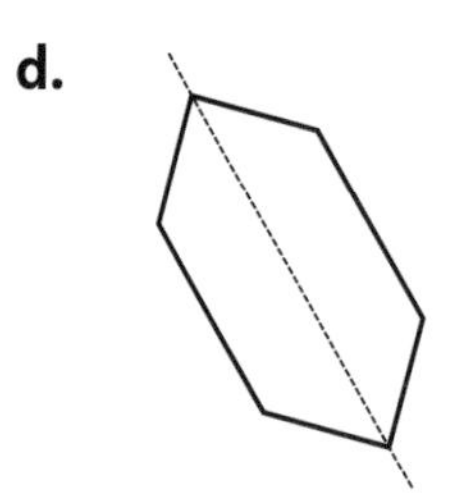

e.

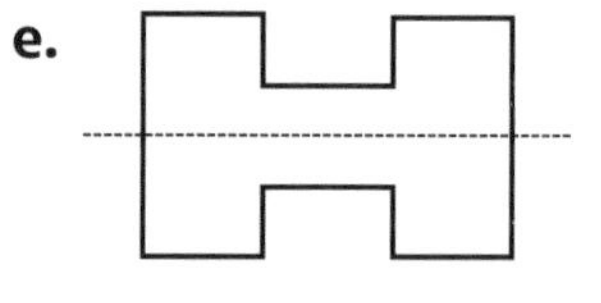

f.

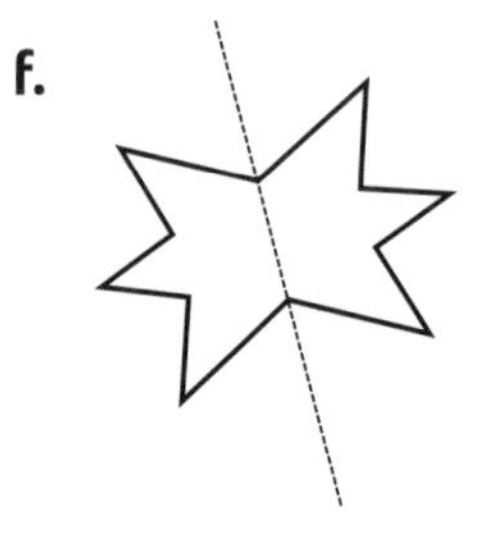

g. 2
h. 3
i. 6
j. 1
k. 1
l. 0

Area

a. $5cm^2$
b. $12cm^2$
c. $12\frac{1}{2}cm^2$
d. $12cm^2$

e.

f.

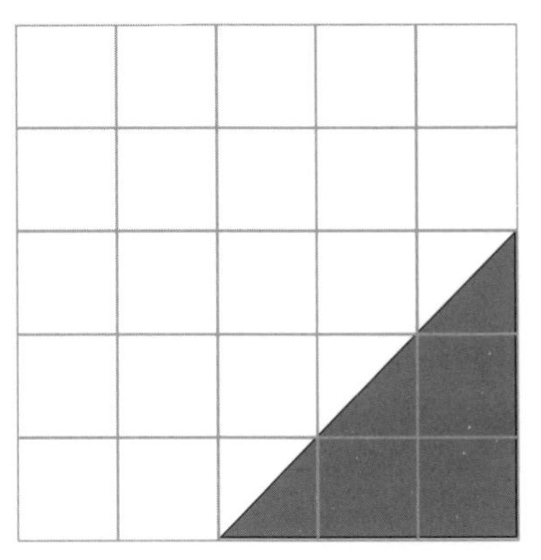

Calculating area using length and width

a. $12cm^2$
b. $12cm^2$
c. $15cm^2$
d. $4cm^2$
e. $10cm^2$
f. $50cm^2$

Perimeter

a. 14cm
b. 16cm
c. 16cm
d. 14cm
e. 10cm

Test 32

a. cm
b. m
c. mm
d. m
e. km
f. Tape measure
g. Trundle wheel
h. Ruler
i. 3cm
j. 5cm
k. 10cm

Test 33

a. l
b. ml
c. cl/ml
d. 12ml
e. 24ml
f. 340ml
g. t/kg
h. kg
i. mg
j. 450g
k. 32kg

Test 34

a. Hours/minutes
b. Seconds
c. Weeks
d. Minutes/hours
e. Half past two, 2.30
f. Twenty past nine, 9.20
g. Quarter past seven, 7.15
h. Five to three, 2.55

Answers

i. 5.15

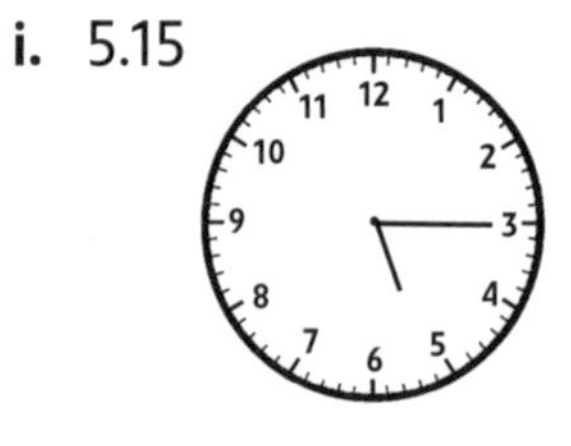

j. 4.00

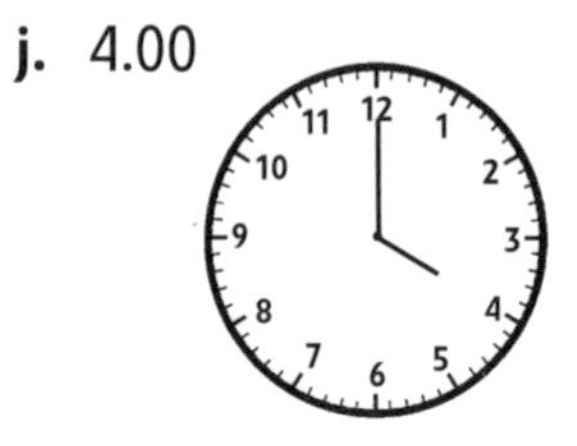

k. 12.30

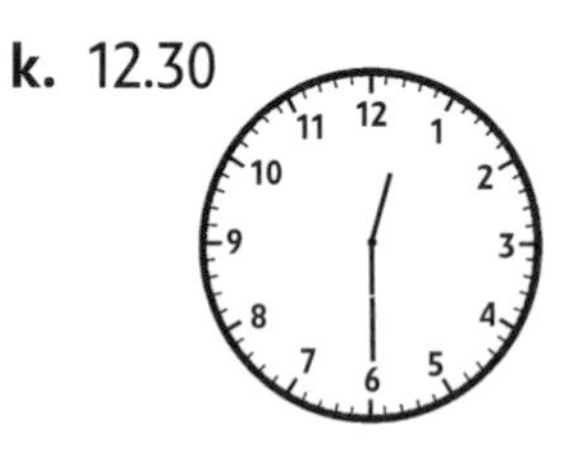

l. 10.25

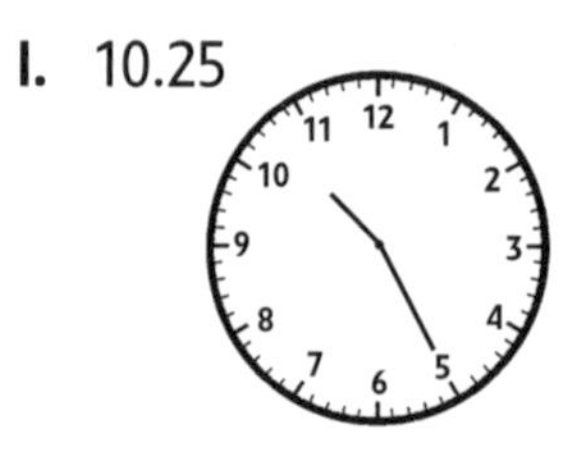

MEASURES: REVISION

Length 1

a. 60mm
b. 100mm
c. 40mm
d. 90mm
e. 15mm
f. 11cm
g. 3cm
h. 24cm
i. 6cm
j. 35cm
k. 400cm
l. 700cm
m. 1000cm
n. 1300cm
o. 2000cm
p. 50cm
q. 6000m
r. 10000m
s. 8000m
t. 15000m

Length 2

a. 11cm
b. 4cm
c. 6cm
d. $10\frac{1}{2}$cm
e. 2cm
f. 9cm
g. 6cm
h. 10cm
i. 5cm
j. $6\frac{1}{2}$cm
k. 8cm

Capacity

a. 100
b. 100
c. 1000
d. 500
e. 300
f. 5000
g. 600
h. 7500
i. 1000
j. 300ml
k. 800ml
l. **a)** 150ml
b) 450ml
m. 200ml

Answers

Mass

a. 1000
b. 1000
c. 1000
d. 1000000
e. 500
f. 250
g. 9000
h. 3500
i. 5000
j. 850g
k. a) 2000g or 2 kg
   b) £6.00 (4 x £1.50)
l. 350g

Time 1

a. 60
b. 60
c. 24
d. 7
e. 52
f. 365
g. 366
h. 10
i. 100
j. 1000
k. 12
l. Fortnight
m. May
n. October
o. July
p. March
q. December
r. February
s. August
t. Spring, summer, autumn, winter

Time 2

a. Half past 8, 8.30
b. Quarter to 6, 5.45
c. Twenty past 9, 9.20
d. 3 o'clock, 3.00
e. Quarter past 2, 2.15
f. Ten to 12, 11.50

Time 3

a. 11.00

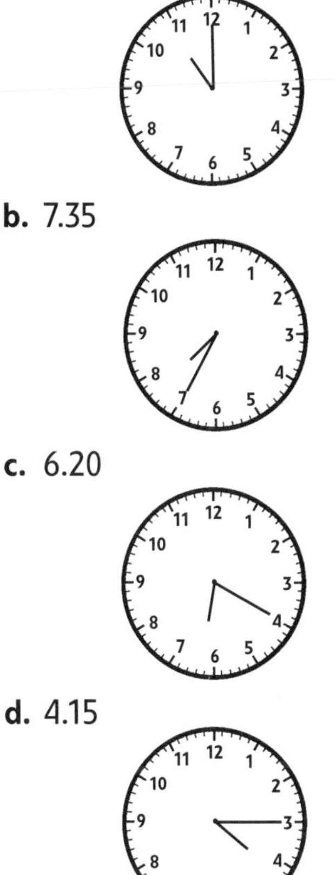

b. 7.35

c. 6.20

d. 4.15

e. 10.30

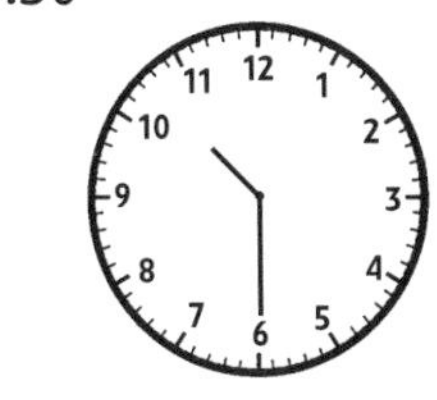

f. 8.40

Answers

Time 4

a. 1.20pm
b. 6.00pm
c. 11.35am
d. 12.35pm
e. 3 hours
f. 6 hours

CHALLENGE!

Milton Keynes - 11.50am
Birmingham - 12.35pm
Sheffield - 12.50pm
Leeds - 1.30pm
Glasgow - 4.30pm